THE
SNOOPERS

THE
SNOOPERS

Fred Stanley Howell

VANTAGE PRESS
New York • Los Angeles

FIRST EDITION

All rights reserved, including the right of
reproduction in whole or in part in any form.

Copyright © 1991 by Fred Stanley Howell

Published by Vantage Press, Inc.
516 West 34th Street, New York, New York 10001

Manufactured in the United States of America
ISBN: 0-533-08896-8

Library of Congress Catalog Card No.: 90-90028

1234567890

To Stuart P. (Stud) Wright,
pilot, engineer, and commanding officer without peer

Contents

THE
SNOOPERS

Prologue

Guadalcanal—Christmas 1942

There were still snipers in the coconut trees, some uncomfortably close to Henderson Field. Washing-machine Charlie came over at least twice every night; Pistol Pete lobbed shells toward the runway on a daily basis; and the Unknown Strafer came across the beach at sunrise two or three times a week.

We had recovered from the invasion of 16 October and the island defenses were reasonably secured by the Thirty-seventh Division and units of the First and Second marine divisions. It was tough to do anything about the air raids, though. The Japanese could put three times as many airplanes in the air as we could any day. The Tokyo Express (Japanese destroyers from Shortland Harbor on the south end of Bougainville) would sweep down the "slot" and shell us in the middle of the night. By daylight they were back in Shortland Harbor, where they were too well protected by ground-based antiaircraft guns and fighters flying out of Kahili airfield for our aircraft to go after them. B-17s staged through Henderson, but by order of COM-AIRSOLS (the navy command that all aircraft in the Solomon Islands were operating under) any B-17 that staged through Henderson was allowed to be on the ground for only one hour. Airborne B-17s were shooting down Japanese fighters at such a rate that the Japanese Navy was desperate to destroy them in any possible way. The Japanese coast watcher on Guadalcanal was ordered to report the arrival of a B-17 immediately

1

upon its landing at Henderson. Then a strike would be ordered and fighters would appear in about an hour in an attempt to destroy the B-17 on the ground.

Christmas day arrived with rotten weather. Scattered squalls swept across Henderson, one after the other; the ceiling was less than 5,000 feet most of the time. Mountains down the ridge of Guadalcanal were sticking up into the clouds and air operations were at a standstill. The tower radio erupted and verified an encoded message that had been received from Buttons, New Hebrides, that a B-17 was approaching Henderson and needed navigation assistance. A primitive approach control radar had been patched together from salvaged ASV radars and was used to align the incoming B-17 with the bomber strip. With some amazement, the pilot broke out of the overcast exactly in line with the runway and in position to make a straight-in approach.

Out of the B-17 appeared a very tall, slim full colonel with sharp, angular features. He wore his rank in plain sight. Several of the mechanics and the engineering officer asked him immediately to please take off the eagles because they didn't want to draw fire from the trees. Many times snipers would sit in the tops of the very tall coconut trees around Henderson just waiting for someone to show up wearing insignia or acting like he was a high-ranking person, and the sniper fire would follow.

The visitor was Col. Stuart P. Wright. Known as 'Stud' by his friends, he was not only a remarkable pilot but an outstanding engineer. Colonel Wright told the engineering officer that he would like to see Admiral Mason, the commander of COM-AIRSOLS. His transportation to the COMAIRSOLS headquarters was quickly arranged, and within a half hour, Colonel Wright was standing at the door of the COMAIRSOLS headquarters operation Quonset hut, putting his insignia back on and getting ready to enter. He told the adjutant that he would like to speak with Admiral Mason and the adjutant led him over to the situation board that the admiral was studying with his staff. Since the Japanese could put three times as many aircraft in the air as could COMAIRSOLS, the admiral was usually deeply concerned with the operations for the next day, or perhaps the next several days, that would maximize the damage to the Japanese and minimize the losses to the U.S. and British units.

Colonel Wright approached the admiral and gave an impeccable salute. Admiral Mason looked up more or less casually and said, "What can I do for you, Colonel?" Colonel Wright replied, "Admiral, we have an outstanding research and development organization back at Wright-Patterson Air Force Base in Ohio. What can we research and develop for you?"

There had been a background of quiet conversation in the Quonset hut until Colonel Wright asked his question, but as if a switch had been thrown, all conversation came to an instant halt. The whole room was frozen, not only silent but motionless: nothing moved, not a sound was heard for about forty seconds. Admiral Mason broke the silence. "Get rid of those fucking Japanese ships!"

Colonel Wright had thought that Admiral Mason would hold a staff conference during which criteria and requirements would be developed for some advanced system that was desperately needed in the war against the Japanese, but Admiral Mason had said it all in those seven words, and that was the end of it.

Colonel Wright stayed at Henderson for three weeks. He experienced the shelling from the "Tokyo Express." He hit the foxholes two or three times every night he was there and he went flying with some of the most experienced B-17 combat pilots in the Eleventh and Fifth groups. When he left the island in January, he knew firsthand the kind of a war we were fighting.

Colonel Wright went back to Wright-Patterson Air Force Base, Ohio, but he was a different man. He pulled together the best pilots and crews from the sea-search squadrons that were operating at that time; he formed a provisional squadron that was named the Wright Project Squadron and he organized and ran a training program that would develop competence within those crews, not only to carry out search missions, but to use

3

the radar and computer that he had installed in the planes to destroy ships. He did all this within seven months, and by August 1943, the Wright Project Squadron was at Guadalcanal. On August 23, 1943, a single "Snooper," which was the nickname given to the Wright Project aircraft and the men who made up the crews, sank two Japanese destroyers trying to sneak down the "slot" to Vella Lavella. From August through December 1943, the Snoopers were credited with more than 34,000 tons of Japanese shipping sunk; more than 8,000 tons probably sunk. Included were an aircraft carrier, two destroyers, two submarines, and two transports. Ships probably sunk included a cruiser, a destroyer, and a submarine. Those damaged included an aircraft carrier, a cruiser, three destroyers, and a submarine. From December 1943 to October 1944, the Japanese pulled back their shipping and naval units from the Allied advance. The Snoopers, operating out of Munda, Momote and Mokerang, had long arduous missions with very little shipping sighted. During that period, though, they did sink 13,000 tons of Japanese shipping; an additional 1,800 tons were probably sunk; 11,000 tons were damaged. From October 1944 to V-J day, the Snoopers operated out of Noemfoor in Geelvink Bay and Morotai in the Halmahera Islands. During that period, the Japanese were trying to supply their troops with sampans and Sugar-Charlies, most of which weighed 500 to 2,000 tons. The Snoopers sank or damaged 119 ships totalling 62,000 tons; thirty-one ships totalling 38,000 tons were probably sunk and 322 ships totalling 110,000 tons were damaged. The largest ship sunk was a 600-foot, 13,000-ton aircraft carrier, which was probably sunk in March 1945.

I have tried to breathe some life into the matter-of-fact but terribly dull mission reports of the Snooper squadron activities from the day they landed on Guadalcanal until V-J day. It is impossible to report, in detail, every operation. I have selected for dramatization, incidents that I was familiar with. The *Snooper News*, a magazine published by Dr. Vince Splaine for the squadron members, has been a source that I drew on when my memory did not adequately retain details.

Guadalcanal

August 1943

Ten airplanes dropped in, not exactly "out of the blue"; in the first place, the sky was seldom blue; in the second place, a lot of people knew they were coming; but ten B-24 heavy bombers with flight crews and twenty electronic technicians arriving with no ground support posed a problem for Col. Bill Matheny, bomber commander of the Thirteenth Air Force. They also posed a problem for Lt. Col. Bob Unruh, commanding officer of the Fifth Heavy Bombardment Group, because the Fifth Group is where Colonel Matheny assigned them.

Over the next month, the planes and crews were at various times called the Wright Project Squadron, the Fifth Group Project Squadron, and the 394th Bombardment Squadron (H). Lieutenant Col. Unruh shuffled airplanes and crews out of the 394th into the other three squadrons of the Fifth Group to make an operating squadron of the "Snoopers."

While the assignment problems and logistic problems were being ironed out, the Snoopers had a job to do. In less than a week, Colonel Matheny ordered a search-and-strike mission for the night of August 27. Three Snooper aircraft were assigned to patrol the "slot" between Guadalcanal and Bougainville Islands. Lieutenant Martus, with Col. Stuart Wright as command pilot, also accompanied by Colonel Matheny; Lieutenant Tillinghast with Lieutenant Colonel Unruh as command pilot; and Captain Lehti with Lieutenant Colonel Burnam as com-

5

mand pilot all took off from Carney Field on Guadalcanal for the search-and-strike mission. Taking off from Carney Field was slightly better than taking off from Henderson. Henderson had a Marston Mat runway; Carney was rolled coral; but taking off in twilight with less than adequate runway lights was no fun in any case.

August 27—Aboard Martus' Aircraft Gremlins Haven— 2100 hours.

Colonel Wright: "What's our altitude, Pilot?"

"We are holding 1,500 feet, sir."

"Bill, are you watching the radar scope?" Colonel Wright asked Colonel Matheny.

"Yes, Stew, and I'm impressed with the range and resolution. It appears to me that we can easily recognize islands 100 miles away."

"Radar to pilot: I have a target at fifty miles range, twenty degrees."

"Roger. Turning to heading of twenty degrees."

"Pilot, this is Colonel Wright. I'd like Radar to watch that target carefully to be sure it is a ship. I haven't seen it move yet, and any Japanese ship in these waters will be moving fast."

"Roger, Colonel. Radar, did you receive that?"

"Radar: Roger."

"Pilot, this is Radar. Take a course of 10 degrees so I can get a look at the target from another angle."

"Pilot: Roger. Ten degrees."

Five minutes of silence.

"Pilot, this is Radar. I think the colonel is correct. The target that I have been following now has a shape that looks more like a small island than a ship. I'm returning to search."

"Pilot: Roger, returning to search heading."

"Bill, this is Stew. This is the first time these crews have searched in this part of the world. After they have had a few missions under their belts, they will know those small islands

6

and not mistake them for ships."

Thirty minutes passed while Lieutenant Martus flew his search heading of 300 degrees, traveling past Russell Island and the New Georgia group. There were so many islands on the radar scope that trying to pick out one that moved was headache-generating.

Aboard Martus' Aircraft—2210 Hours

"Radar to pilot: I have a possible target at 10 degrees on the scope—range, thirty miles. It's a ship, but it must be a small cargo ship. The return isn't strong enough for a Japanese naval vessel."

"Roger, Radar. I'm turning toward the target. Colonel Wright, do you verify that he has a valid target?"

"Roger, Pilot. Let's go get him!"

"Pilot to bombardier: Are you ready to drop?"

"Bombardier to pilot: Roger, give me drop altitude."

"Pilot to bombardier: Drop altitude will be 1,500 feet above the surface."

"Bombardier. Roger. API is engaged. Target is on my scope. Computer is armed. I estimate drop in eight minutes."

"Stew, this is Bill. How can the pilot be so sure that he is 1,500 feet above the surface?"

"This airplane is equipped with a radar altimeter, Bill. It is much more accurate than the barometric altimeter. On long missions, the baro-altimeter can be off a thousand feet or more, but the radar altimeter will always be accurate to twenty-five feet or less. At 1,500 feet altitude, where we are now, it is accurate to about ten feet."

"Pilot to bombardier: I'm going to follow your API manually, I won't hook you into the autopilot for this run."

"Bombardier. Roger, keep it centered. We are about five minutes from drop."

"Bombardier. Three minutes. I have armed five of our 500 pounders and I'll set the intervalometer to twenty-five feet.

7

That should put two of them on his deck."

"Bombardier. One minute to drop."

The target return was moving very determinedly down the vertical crosshair on the bombardier's scope. When it reached the horizontal crosshair, the computer would trigger the intervalometer and a string of five five-hundred-pound bombs would be on their way to meet the Japanese ship.

"Bomb-bay doors open," sang out the bombardier.

"Verify bomb-bay doors open," echoed the navigator.

"Bombs away!"

Gremlin's Haven surged upward as 2,500 pounds of dead weight were released. It takes less than seven seconds for a bomb to reach the ground from an altitude of 1,500 feet. The explosions of the five bombs were felt solidly inside the airplane. Lieutenant Martus banked sharply after the bombs left the bomb bay so that he and the waist gunner and the navigator could get a view of the target in the light of the bombs. They all agreed that the first bomb hit the ship, but the other four flew over the ship and landed in the water.

"Pilot, this is Colonel Wright. See if you can raise Lieutenant Tillinghast or Captain Lehti on the radio. I'd like to see if they have had any luck."

"Colonel Wright, this is the pilot. I have been listening to Lieutenant Tillinghast and Captain Lehti make their reports to headquarters. Captain Lehti dropped on a target that turned out to be a small island in the light of their bombs. Lieutenant Tillinghast could not find a suitable target. He dropped his bombs on Rekata."

"Thank you, Lieutenant. Let's head for home."

Thus ended Snooper mission one. Not a very auspicious beginning. New crews were operating a new weapon system in an unfamiliar theater, but it was not a total failure; the 500-pound bomb that hit the Sugar-Charlie and the bombs that entered the water close to the ship caused major damage.

August 28, 1943—13th Bomber Command Headquarters—1300 Hours

Colonel Matheny had called Colonel Wright to his "office" (a Quonset hut in the coconut grove) to discuss the previous night's operation and to plan for the immediate future.

"Stew, I was much impressed with the operation last night. That radar equipment and the way the crews handled themselves on the very first combat operation give me hope that we have a leg up on the Japanese naval forces. Can we keep an umbrella over the Solomons with Snoopers?"

"Bill, I have a lot of faith in the crews and the equipment that the Snoopers are flying. If you give Lieutenant Colonel Unruh and me the order to attack any Japanese shipping that moves in the Solomons, the Snoopers will make every effort to do just that."

"All right, Stew, you've got it. I'll call Bob Unruh and tell him to consult with you and plan for the maximum use of the Snoopers to end the 'Tokyo Express'. "

5th Group G-3 (Operations Office)—1500 Hours

Colonel Wright, Lieutenant Colonel Unruh and Maj. Leo J. (Bill) Foster, commanding officer of the Wright Project Squadron, discussed the limits that could be expected of the Snoopers.

Colonel Wright opened the discussion. "Major Foster, how many Snooper aircraft can we expect to have flying search-and-attack missions on a day-to-day basis?"

"Sir, I think we can have three aircraft flying on a night-by-night basis. Remember, this is the very first time that microwave radar has ever been operated in a field situation like we have here in the Solomons. This is the first time some of that equipment has been permanently removed from major maintenance facilities. I have a lot of faith in the technicians we

9

brought with us, but nobody really knows what will happen to the radar and the computers under the sloppy weather conditions here in the Solomons."

"How about those field representatives who came with you from Westinghouse and Bell labs?" Lieutenant Colonel Unruh asked.

"Pappy Clark and Doc Sharkey are the most knowledgeable engineers in the world when it comes to this specific equipment, and I think they will be a big help to the military technicians, but I hesitate to predict that we will have 100 percent operation of the Snooper gear."

"Colonel Wright, do you agree with Major Foster?"

"I think Bill is being somewhat conservative, Bob, but I have to agree with him that field operations are much more difficult than operating out of a clean, well-stocked depot. At the same time, one of the things we will be testing is the ability of equipment and maintenance procedures to allow operations to be conducted in the field. Let's start out with a schedule of three aircraft per night and see how it works."

"I'll agree, with the stipulation that we review the operations every week to see if we need to make changes."

"Major Foster, I will issue operation orders on a daily basis beginning tomorrow night. If A-2 [army intelligence] alerts us to major Japanese activity, I'll order you to have all available aircraft in the air, perhaps on very short notice."

August 29—1800 Hours

Three Snoopers took off from Carney field for search-and-attack missions. Capt. Frank Reynolds and crew flew northwest up the south side of the Solomons to Buka Passage; Lt. Charles Rockwood flew the "slot" from Guadalcanal to Bougainville; and Lt. George Tillinghast took the north side of the Solomons to Buka. Radar operators on Reynold's and Tillinghast's flights reported that they did not see any targets that they could identify as ships. The radar operator on Rockwell's flight reported a malfunction of the radar about an hour into the mission, and Rockwell was forced to return to Carney.

August 30—Carney Field—0600 Hours

The failure of Lieutenant Rockwell's radar on his first mission caused much concern in the whole Snooper squadron. As soon as the sun was up, the radar operator, three radar technicians, and Pappy Clark were examining the radar to determine the cause of the failure.

The transmitted pulses from the magnetron were carried to the antenna by solid coaxial cable. It was solid except for one place; because the radar transmitter had to be shock mounted to prevent damage from engine vibration and the shocks of landing, there had to be one joint that would give enough to allow the shock mounts to be effective. This joint was called a woggle joint. It consisted of a set of reed-shaped contacts that connected one side of the woggle joint to the other side. There was a flexible hose that was clamped on each side of the woggle joint, because the whole length of the solid coaxial cable had to be pressurized with dry nitrogen to prevent corrosion and to prevent arcing under the electrical stress of the high-power transmitted pulses. The trouble with Rockwell's radar had been that arcing at the reed contacts of the woggle joint had progressively destroyed the conducting properties of the coax.

Pappy Clark recognized this problem as one he had seen when he performed field engineering at Boca Raton, Florida. The remedy was to coat the area that the reed contacts pressed against with a conducting lubricant. Disassembling the coax, cleaning the contacts, and applying the lubricant took most of the morning. When the radar was checked out and found to be operating properly, a larger problem had to be faced. Since Rockwell's radar had failed, there was no way of knowing whether all the other radars would perform properly without the lubricant being applied.

Pappy Clark, the assigned radar officer, Capt. Ray Barriere, and the master sergeant in charge of the radar technicians, Floyd Hune, all reported to the commanding officer, Major Foster. Captain Barriere spoke first.

"Sir, I recommend that all the aircraft be declared out of commission until we can lubricate the woggle joints. If we try to fly them as they are, I expect that we will have a high rate of failures; we might even have some woggle joints damaged so badly that they will have to be replaced, and we do not have 100 percent spares of that particular part."

"Well, Ray, how long will it take you and your technicians to lubricate all the woggle joints?" Major Foster asked.

"It took Pappy and three technicians almost six hours to do the job on Rockwell's airplane. I would expect, now that we know what the problem is, that three techs can do the job in about four hours per airplane."

"How many techs can you put on it, Ray?"

"We have five radar techs right now. I can work with two of them, and with two crews we can have Rockwell's airplane and two others ready by 2000 hours tonight."

"Let me talk to Lieutenant Colonel Unruh and see if he will postpone takeoff time to 2000 hours."

Lieutenant Colonel Unruh agreed. Three crews were assigned to the search-and-strike mission for the night of August 30 and 31. Lt. Robert Easterling was assigned the "slot" search. Maj. Fran Carlson was assigned the search on the north side of the Solomons, and Lt. George Tillinghast was assigned the search on the south side of the Solomons.

Three airplanes were serviced and ready to fly by 1900 hours. In spite of weather that had turned rotten, with rain squalls racing down Sealark Channel on the north side of Guadalcanal, and the ceiling nearly zero altitude, the woggle joints were lubricated and all mechanical checks were completed on the three designated aircraft. At 2000 hours they were on their way.

August 31—0200 Hours

Maj. Leo Foster, the commanding officer of the Wright Project Squadron, entered the operations tent and spoke to Capt. John Zinn, who was the operations duty officer.

"Any word from the mission, John?"

"Thirteenth Bomber Command has been in touch with me all night, Bill. Tillinghast dropped on a target that they later identified as a small island. Carlson didn't see any identifiable targets so he dropped on his secondary, that runway on the south side of New Georgia. I'm worried about Easterling. He called in and said he was attacking a convoy. After the attack, Command said that messages from Easterling have been garbled."

"Let's give Command a call and see if they have any more word."

Captain Zinn cranked up the EE-8 field phone.

"Operator, give me Thirteenth Bomber Command Operations."

"Operations, this is Wright Project Squadron Operations. Do you have any further information on aircraft *839?*"

"Roger, thank you."

"Bill, they say that since the last garbled message that they received about two hours ago, they haven't heard a sound from Easterling. I think we should get out to the runway and wait for him."

"Okay, John, the duty sergeant can take phone messages until we get back."

Major Foster and Captain Zinn climbed into the operations jeep and headed out to the end of the runway at Carney. The drive over the rutted, muddy track through the coconut trees with blackout headlights that barely made a glow in the dark was maddening. They finally arrived at the approach end of the runway and huddled in the jeep against the occasional squall that would dump lashing rain on them.

At 0310 the running lights of an airplane could be seen approaching from the northwest.

"My God, he's flying awfully low, John. He must be in trouble!" Major Foster said, his voice showing deep concern. As he uttered those words, the right wing of the aircraft dipped, caught in a coconut tree, and the aircraft spun to the ground. The resulting crash and fire killed everyone on board.

August 31—0800 Hours

The mood among the Snoopers was solemn. Every member of the squadron knew that there would be losses, but losing the Easterling crew so soon shook everyone up. Colonel Wright had told the crews before they left the U.S. that losses might run as high as 75 percent, but nobody goes into combat thinking that he will be one of the casualties.

There was very little left to analyze at the crash site. The number three engine had been feathered. It had probably been damaged by antiaircraft fire. The crew were so badly mangled by the crash or burned by the fire that very little could be concluded about the cause of the crash. In discussing the last few radio messages heard from aircraft *839*, Lieutenant Easterling was not the one who transmitted the messages. It was possible that the pilot and perhaps the copilot were dead from antiaircraft fire and one of the other crew members had tried to fly the plane home.

September

In spite of the loss of Lieutenant Easterling's airplane and crew, three Snooper aircraft were ready for search-and-strike missions every night. Three missions were flown every night from September 1 to September 27 with the result that ten ships were sunk or damaged. About half were Japanese capital ships, destroyers, cruisers, and large cargo ships.

September 20—The Mystery of the Inverter Failures

The radar and the computers on the Snooper aircraft required 120–volt 400-cycle AC power. Four hundred cycle power was used to allow smaller transformers and smaller filter capacitors, thus reducing the weight that had to be carried by the aircraft. The primary power on the aircraft was twenty-eight volts DC. An inverter was installed on each aircraft to convert the twenty-eight volts DC to 120 volts 400-cycle power. This inverter was mounted under the flight deck and was a constant source of complaints from the flight deck crews because it was in the way for anyone who needed to get into the "greenhouse" up in the front of the aircraft. It was also noisy and when not properly adjusted gave off a grinding noise on any radio gear in the aircraft.

As the Snoopers moved into September, some of the crews reported that the inverters were blowing the circuit breakers. Several missions were aborted when the circuit breakers on the inverters opened and all attempts to get them restarted failed. Examination of these inverters showed that the bearings on the shaft that ran through the center of the armature had been overheated and had produced so much drag on the twenty-eight volt drive motor that the current drain from the aircraft bus exceeded the allowable. The bearings had gotten hot enough to bake out the lubricating grease, and as soon as that happened, the drag on the bearings increased to the point that the circuit breakers opened.

These overheated bearings became a mystery that everyone talked about in the maintenance Quonset. The mystery was that the inverters had been very dependable in the sea-search missions off the coast of the U.S. and they had been dependable on the long flights from the U.S. to Guadalcanal. Now that the Snoopers were going into combat almost every night, the inverters were failing; but they didn't fail every time, and the irregularity was the mystery.

Pappy Clark was working on the problem harder than anyone. Since he was the representative of Western Electric Company, and since it was Western Electric equipment that was giving trouble, everyone was looking to him for a solution.

Pappy came into the maintenance Quonset early the morning of sixteen September. "It's the ones that have been shot at that fail!" he literally shouted to all the maintenance crew.

Everyone looked up at him, astonished. Master Sergeant Hune finally spoke up.

"What the hell are you talking about, Pappy?"

"I've been keeping a log of the operations and I'm getting a strong correlation between the crews that report heavy antiaircraft fire when they attack a ship and the failures of the inverters."

"Pappy, those inverters aren't being hit by antiaircraft fire. We would see damage other than the overheated bearings if that was so," replied Hune.

"It isn't the direct result of the antiaircraft fire," said Pappy. "It's what the pilots do when they are being fired on."

"What do they do?"

"They take violent evasive action!" replied Pappy. "The armatures on those inverters weigh forty-five pounds and they spin at 4,000 rpm. The gyroscopic effect is awesome. When the pilot rolls the aircraft to avoid the antiaircraft fire, he overloads the bearings on the inverter and cooks the grease out of them. After that it is only a matter of time before the bearings start dragging and the breaker opens."

"That is all well and good, Pappy," said Master Sergeant Hune. "But we can't very well ask the pilots to quit taking evasive action, can we?"

"We don't have to," replied Pappy. "Those inverters are mounted with the shafts lateral to the flight path. That puts the full force of the gyro effect on the bearings when the pilot rolls the aircraft. All we have to do is remount the inverters with the shaft in line with the flight path, and the gyro effect will be minimized."

Master Sergeant Hune called Captain Barriere and talked it over with him. He immediately grasped the significance of Pappy's analysis and ordered all the inverters to be mounted with the rotating shafts parallel to the flight path of the aircraft.

The mystery of the failed inverters had been solved.

Tokyo Express—You've Had It!

Carney Field—September 28—1400 Hours

The call went out to the whole Snooper squadron: "All flight crews, meet in the mess hall, on the double!"

It was necessary to hold "all flight crews" meetings in the mess hall because it was the only place, other than the Fifth Group movie theater, that would hold the four to five hundred men who would show up. Colonel Matheny was there and addressed the squadron; by that date they had been designated the 394th.

"Men of the 394th, we have received word from A-2 [army intelligence] that they have intercepted and decoded a message from the Japanese navy command at Rabaul ordering a task force to assemble at Buka Passage and to proceed to the island of Kiota with the purpose of reinforcing their garrison. I am hereby ordering the 394th Heavy Bombardment Squadron to deploy all available Snooper aircraft. You will search and strike the task force and, if at all possible, prevent them from accomplishing their assigned task."

"Major Foster, how many aircraft can you deploy for this mission?"

"Sir, we have eight aircraft in operational standby. We can deploy all eight," Major Foster replied.

"Bob, you will cut an operational order to that effect," said Colonel Matheny to Lt. Col. Bob Unruh.

"Yes, sir!" sang out Lieutenant Colonel Unruh. "Snoopers, be ready for taxi and takeoff at 1700 hours."

"Pilots and navigators, report to the operations hut for detailed instructions. The rest of you get ready for the mission. Major Carlson has the situation maps and the estimate of the strength of the task force. He will brief the pilots and navigators. You are dismissed," said Major Foster.

1700 Hours

"Carney tower, this is aircraft number *832*, request permission for taxi and takeoff of 394th Squadron," said Major Foster.

"Roger, *832*. You are clear for taxi and takeoff."

"Carney, *854*. Request permission to taxi and takeoff," said Capt. John Zinn.

"Roger, *854*. Clear."

"Carney, *833*. Request permission to taxi and takeoff," said Capt. Robert Lehti.

"Roger, *822*. Clear."

"Carney, *833*. Request permission to taxi and takeoff," said Capt. Frank Reynolds.

"Roger, *833*. Clear."

"Carney, *838*. Request permission to taxi and takeoff," said Charles Rockwood.

"Roger, *838*. Clear."

"Carney, *653*. Request permission to taxi and takeoff," said Lt. Fred Martus.

"Roger *653*. Clear."

"Carney, *651*. Request permission to taxi and takeoff," said Lt. Ken Brown.

"Roger, *651*. Clear."

Lt. Durward Sumner and crew were in aircraft number *851*. Lieutenant Sumner had been transferred to the Snoopers from the 307th Group, and because he was flying with a new crew and an aircraft with an unfamiliar configuration, he and the crew chief took an extra two hours to be sure they were following the checklist properly. By 1740 hours the first seven Snoopers were airborne, but *851* wasn't ready to taxi until 1930 hours. An alert called by the air defense radar delayed them until 2115. At 2140: "Carney Tower, this is aircraft number *851*, request permission to taxi and takeoff," said Lieutenant Sumner.

"Roger, *851*. You are clear."

851 was off the ground at 2144 hours.

On Board Aircraft *833*—Capt. Frank Reynolds, Pilot—1920 Hours

"Radar to pilot: I have eleven targets traveling in line on a course of 160 degrees. Distance forty miles at ten o'clock."

Captain Reynolds: "Roger, Radar. Give me a mark when the last target in the line is at nine o'clock. I want to make a beam run on him. Bombardier, did you read that?"

"Roger, Frank. Give me a mark when he is dead ahead at thirty miles."

"Roger, George. Will do."

Ten minutes of silence.

"Radar to pilot: Nine o'clock, thirty-five miles range."

"Pilot to crew: I'm turning ninety degrees left. Radar, you will lose the target until I level out. It should be dead ahead at thirty plus miles."

Captain Reynolds made a sharp left turn, which took less than thirty seconds. Then he leveled out.

"Pilot to crew: we are level at 1,300 feet altitude. The target should be dead ahead. George, get ready to track and drop. Radar, are we on course?"

"Radar to pilot: The target is on a southerly course. Correct five degrees left."

"Roger. George, are you ready to drop?"

"Roger, Frank. I've armed six bombs and set the intervalometer at seventy-five feet spacing. The API is on and I have the target in my scope. Radar, give me a thirty-degree sector scan at twelve o'clock."

"Radar. Roger."

"Opening bomb-bay doors," sang out the bombardier.

"Verify bomb-bay doors open," echoed the navigator.

Captain Reynolds was holding the aircraft altitude at 1,300

feet and keeping the API centered so the target moved down the vertical cross-hair of the bombardier's scope.

At an airspeed of 135 knots, it takes twelve minutes to move thirty miles. The ship was blacked out and the weather was overcast. At 1,300 feet altitude, Captain Reynolds was moving in and out of the low clouds. The only indication of the ship's presence was the radar return. Apparently the captain of the ship felt safe in the poor visibility because he made no attempt to evade the Snooper.

"Bombardier to pilot: One minute to drop."

"Roger, George."

The radar return marched down the vertical cross-hair on the bombardier's scope. When it hit the horizontal cross-hair, the computer sent the drop signal to the intervalometer.

"Bombs away!"

Captain Reynolds made a steep banking turn to give the navigator, top turret gunner, and the waist gunner a chance to identify the ship in the light of the bomb blast, but when the six 500-pound bombs dropped from the bomb bay of *833*, the aircraft surged upward and entered the low cloud deck. By the time Captain Reynolds had leveled out and descended out of the clouds, they were too far away to see much except that the ship was on fire. They also saw antiaircraft fire coming from one of the other ships in the task force, but it was not directed at *833*.

On Board Aircraft *838*—Lieutenant Charles L. Rockwood, Pilot—1920 Hours

"Radar to Pilot: I have eleven ships traveling in line on the scope, forty-five miles range at ten o'clock."

"Roger, Radar, Give me a mark when they are at nine o'clock."

"Don, are you ready to drop when we get lined up?"

"Roger, Rocky. I'll arm three bombs and set the intervalometer spacing at seventy-five feet. What altitude will we be at?"

"Roger, Don. I'm going in at one thousand feet altitude. There are other Snoopers in the vicinity. I'm going to follow Frank. Maybe the ack-ack will be less with both of us going in at the same time."

"Radar to pilot: I have lots of rabbits on the screen." (The radar operator was referring to transmitted pulses from other Snooper aircraft. These pulses are referred to as running rabbits. They usually did not interfere with the operation of the Snooper radar because they were so random. The direction and distance of nearby Snoopers could be interpreted by knowledgeable radar operators.)

"Roger, Radar, are you able to keep the target in view?" Lieutenant Rockwood was worried about losing the target due to the other radar's interference.

"The other radar just went to sector scan, sir, and the interference is not bothering me now. Which ship do you want a nine o'clock mark on?"

"Give me a mark when the last ship in the line is at nine o'clock."

"Roger."

"Rocky, let's make our run on the second-from-last ship. I think Frank will take the last ship, and he is ahead of us," said Don Desko.

"Roger, Don. Radar, did you copy Lieutenant Desko?"

"Roger. Ship number two is at the nine o'clock position." A pause, then: "Now!"

"Roger, radar. Turning toward target. Watch for it to show up at twelve o'clock in about thirty seconds."

Sometimes thirty seconds can seem like a long time.

"We're level. Radar, report," said Lieutenant Rockwood.

"Radar to pilot: Target three degrees left, range thirty-eight miles."

"Radar, this is the bombardier. Give me a thirty-degree sector scan at twelve o'clock. I have the target, Rocky."

"Roger, Don. We are at one thousand feet altitude and I'll hold it here for the run."

"Roger, Rocky. Opening bomb-bay doors."

"Verify bomb-bay doors open," said navigator Lt. Mark Dennis.

"Radar to pilot: Rabbits from *833* are to our right. I can't keep track of him now while the radar is on sector scan."

"Roger, Radar. *833* is at 1,300 feet altitude and is attacking the trailing ship. We will be about a mile south of him and at a lower attitude. It looks like we will both be dropping at about the same time."

"Bombardier to pilot: Three minutes to drop, Rocky."

"Roger, Don."

"Rocky, this target is getting bigger and bigger on my screen, I'm going to aim at the stern: Maybe we can hit the engine room."

"Don't get fancy, Don. Just be sure you hit it."

"Okay, Rocky. Amidships it is. Thirty seconds to drop."

Another long thirty seconds.

"Bombs away!"

Lieutenant Rockwood made a left turn.

"Holy cow, that was a big mother! I think it was a converted aircraft carrier" navigator Mark Dennis yelled into the intercom line. "Two bombs hit just aft of amidships, but I didn't see any fire."

"Are we getting any return fire from the task force?" asked Lieutenant Rockwood.

"There are tracers coming up from other ships in the task force," reported Lieutenant Dennis, "but I can't tell if they're shooting at us and falling short or if they're shooting at someone else."

"Pilot to crew: I'm going to make a circle around the task force and stand far enough off to give the other Snoopers room to make their runs without interference from us. Radar, go to search mode."

"Radar. Roger."

Lieutenant Rockwood made a wide search pattern to the north side of the New Georgia Islands. There were no detectable ships in the area. While he was searching, he was listening to the Snooper frequency. He heard Captain John Zinn report his attack on the task force at 2012 hours; he heard Lieutenant Martus report that he was starting an attack at 2030 hours, but there was no report of results; he heard Major Foster report his attack on the task force at 2034; Captain Lehti reported that he started a bombing run, but his IFF was interrogated and he broke off the attack because he was afraid he was attacking a friendly ship.

At 2035, just after Major Foster made his attack, Lieutenant Rockwell queried his radar operator.

"Radar, this is the pilot. Do you have the task force on the scope?"

"Roger. I see only nine ships in the task force now. They are at forty miles ten degrees left."

"Don, are you ready to drop on another ship?"

"Roger, Rocky, we have three bombs left. I'll arm them and set the intervalometer to fifty feet. Radar, give me a thirty-degree sector scan at twelve o'clock."

"Radar. Roger."

"Rocky, I'm going to drop on the trailing ship; the API is engaged and I have the target on my screen."

"Opening bomb-bay doors," said Lieutenant Desko. "What is our altitude, Rocky?"

"I'm going in at 1,500 feet altitude, Don. There was a lot of ack-ack when Major Foster made his run, so I'd rather not be down at 1,000."

"Roger, Rocky. I'm set up for drop in five minutes."

Five minutes later:

"Bombs away!"

Lieutenant Rockwood made a tight right turn, which allowed the top turret gunner and the tail gunner to see the target in the light of the bomb blast.

"Top Turret to pilot: she rolled over and sank!"

"Tail Gunner to pilot: I saw her sink too!"

"Pilot to crew: Can anyone identify the type of ship?"

"Navigator to pilot: It looked like a destroyer to me!"

"Top Turret: I agree."

"Tail Gunner: I agree too."

"Okay, crew, that was a good job. We don't have any bombs left, so give me a course to base, Navigator."

"Navigator. Roger; take a course of 130, we should see the BUPS beacon in about thirty minutes."

"Roger, turning to 130."

On board Aircraft *854*—Capt. John Zinn, Pilot—1935 Hours

"Radar to pilot: I have nine ships in line at two o'clock, range thirty miles."

"Roger, Radar. Give me a mark when they are at five o'clock. I'm going to swing around them and make a run on the trailing ship from the rear."

"Radar. Roger."

It took fifteen minutes for *854* to move behind the task force. At 1950:

"Radar to pilot: Trailing ship is at five o'clock."

"Roger, Radar. I'm going to turn 180; you'll lose the targets for about a minute. I'll give you a mark when we are level again."

"Radar. Roger."

"Sam, are you set for a bombing run?" Captain Zinn asked Lieutenant Pelligrini, the bombardier.

"Roger, John. I have armed all six of our bombs. What altitude should I set into the computer?"

"I'm at 1,300 feet now, Sam. I'll hold it during the run."

"Roger. Thirteen hundred."

Almost a full minute passed as Captain Zinn turned behind the task force.

"Pilot to crew: We are level at 1,300 feet; Radar, where is the target?"

"Radar to pilot: Trailing ship is ten degrees left at thirty-five miles."

"Roger, Radar. Turning ten degrees left. Sam, do you have the target in view?"

"Roger, John. Radar, give me a thirty-degree sector scan at twelve o'clock."

"Radar. Roger."

854 was approaching a destroyer, and from the rear it presented a very narrow target to the radar. Lieutenant Pelligrini had a difficult time keeping the vertical cross-hair on the ship's radar return. There was more turbulence from the stack exhausts of the nine ships as they steamed down the channel.

"John, I'm having a tough time keeping the target centered in azimuth."

"I've been noticing the API doing some waving around. Keep at it—I don't want to make more than one pass at these guys."

"Okay, John. Three minutes to drop; bomb-bay doors opening."

"Verify bomb-bay doors open," responded navigator Lt. James Pope.

"One minute to drop," said Lieutenant Pelligrini.

One minute—

"Bombs away!"

Captain Zinn banked sharply to the right as soon as the bombs left the bomb-bay. *854* had zoomed up into the overcast with the weight of the bombs gone, and Captain Zinn pushed forward on the wheel to get under the cloud cover.

"It looks like they all hit on the right side of the ship," reported the top turret gunner. "The closest one was the first one, but it was about thirty feet away from the right side of the ship."

"Roger, Top Turret. Can anyone else confirm that?" asked Captain Zinn.

"Tail Turret. That is the same thing as I saw."

"Waist Gun. Agree."

"Okay, Crew. Hope we have better luck next time. Jim, give me a course to Carney."

"Roger, John. Take a course of 110. We should see the BUPS beacon in about thirty minutes."

"Roger, Jim. Turning to 110."

On Board Aircraft *832*—Maj. Leo J. Bill Foster, Pilot—1925 Hours

"Radar to pilot: I have a string of targets between Bougainville and Choiseul, but they look like reefs on the screen. Can anyone see them? They are at twenty miles at two o'clock."

"Pilot to radar: visibility is too poor to visually identify. Stand by." Major Foster called on the air-to-air radio, "*833*, what is the position of your target? This is *832*."

"*832*, we are going for a string of ships at six degrees, thirty-three minutes south and one hundred fifty-six degrees seventeen minutes east."

"Roger, *833*. Thank you."

"Radar, go back to that target you designated. Captain Reynolds has verified that it is the task force." Major Foster was back on the intercom.

"Radar. Roger. The target is at four o'clock, range between forty and fifty miles."

"Keep them in sight, Radar, but keep searching. I'm going to make a sweep around behind them and we'll go after them when the other Snoopers have moved out of the area."

"Radar. Roger."

Captain Reynolds departed the area of the task force after dropping all of his bombs at 1945 hours. Lieutenant Rockwood still had three bombs left when he started the broad sweep toward the New Georgia Islands. Captain Zinn had dropped all his bombs, and Lieutenant Martus was not heard from after his radio message at 2015 hours announcing the beginning of a run on the task force. At 2020 hours, Major Foster called the radar operator.

"Radar, do you still have the task force in sight?"

"Radar. Roger. Trailing ship in the line is now at three o'clock, range fifty-five miles."

"Roger, Radar. Pilot to crew: I'm going to swing around behind the task force and make a rear-quartering run on the tail-end Charlie. Cecil, are you ready to drop?" (Lt. Cecil Cothran was the bombardier.)

"Roger, Bill. I have armed all six bombs, and I'm waiting for the target to appear on my scope."

"Radar to pilot: The trailing target is ten degrees left at thirty-five miles."

"Roger, Radar. Turning ten degrees left. Ceese, it should be showing up on your scope."

"Roger, Bill. I have the target. API is engaged. Bomb-bay doors open. I estimate nine minutes to drop."

"Verify bomb-bay doors open," replied John Thompson, navigator.

"Bill, are we still at 1,500 feet altitude? asked Lieutenant Cothran.

"Roger, Ceese."

"Good. That's what I had set into the computer and I just wanted to make sure. Three minutes."

"We've got some tracers coming up at us, Bill!"

"Roger, Ceese, stay with it."

"Bombs away!

"We're catching a lot of attention from those gunners, Bill. They're just filling the air with ack-ack, but some of it is coming pretty close."

Major Foster had rolled the airplane over to the right as soon as Lieutenant Cothran had given the bombs-away signal. As soon as the bombs hit and exploded, the antiaircraft fire ceased. In the light of the bomb blasts, the ship was identified as a destroyer with two slanting stacks. Four of the six bombs were seen to impact on the target. Before leaving the area, Major Foster took a look around the area and observed three fires burning.

On Board Aircraft *822*—Captain Robert Lehti, Pilot—1920 Hours

"Pilot, this is Radar. I have a line of targets dead ahead at thirty miles. I can't verify that they are ships."

"Roger, Radar. I'll make a pass at them and see what they are."

"Bob, this is Werner. I got a visual glimpse of those targets and they are definitely ships."

"Roger, Butch. I'll make a swing around and set up a bombing run. We are at 1,400 feet altitude."

"Roger, Bob. I've armed all six bombs. Give me a mark when they should show up on my scope."

"Roger, Butch."

Ten minutes passed.

"Radar, this is the pilot. We should be approaching the target now."

"Radar. Roger. I have the target five degrees right at thirty-eight miles."

"You should have him on your scope, Butch."

"Roger, Bob. API is engaged. Opening bomb-bay doors."

"Verify bomb-bay doors open," said Lieutenant Carl Rose, navigator.

"Range to target, ten miles, Bob."

"Roger, Butch."

"Pilot to Crew! Abort the run, I have IFF interrogation. We may be engaging a friendly ship."

"Roger, Bob. Arming is off; bomb-bay doors closing."

"Carl, put me on a course for Buka Passage, and we'll hunt for stragglers."

"Roger, Bob. Take a course of 340 until I get a radar fix."

Captain Lehti searched the north coast of Bougainville for

ships but none appeared. At 2100 hours:

"Carl, this is Bob. Give me a heading for Carney. I'm going to call it a night."

"Roger, Bob. Take a course of 200 degrees. The BUPS beacon should show up in about forty-five minutes."

That was the end of the Tokyo Express in the Solomon Islands. In a matter of three hours, eight Snoopers had sunk four Japanese capital ships, possibly sunk a fifth, and taught the Japanese naval command that darkness and bad weather were no longer hiding places.

Snoopers on the Move

General Nathan F. Twining, commanding general of the Thirteenth Air Force, knew that the Japanese had an airfield closer than Kahili. Kahili was located on the southeast end of Bougainville, 385 miles from Carney. Under cruise power settings, the fighters that were based at Kahili would need at least two hours to make it to Carney, but often fighters would show up just over an hour after the coast watcher sent them a message regarding unusual activity at Henderson, Carney, or in the shipping channel.

The Eighteenth Photo Reconnaissance Squadron, based at Henderson, made flight after flight to try to discover where the nearer airfield was. All of their efforts came to naught until April 1943 when a stereo viewer that allowed three dimensional viewing of the whole Solomon Island Chain arrived at the squadron.

A runway suddenly jumped out of the stereo photographs of New Georgia Island, where the Munda coconut plantation was located. The runway was there, but it looked like there were coconut trees growing right on the runway as well as around it. A special mission was flown by the Eighteenth to get some close-up, low-level pictures of the runway. These pictures showed that the coconut trees that seemed to be growing on the runway, and therefore hiding it from high-altitude photography, were in fact mounted on sleds! When the runway was not in use the coconut trees would be towed out and lined up with the other trees on the plantation; when the runway was in use, the trees would be towed out of the way.

General Twining asked the Fourteenth Army Corps to invade the island and put the runway out of commission. That was done late in July. A large area around the runway was secured and a U.S. Navy construction battalion turned Munda into one of the best runways in the South Pacific. The Snoopers were ordered to move to Munda in December 1943.

Moving a heavy bombardment squadron from one airdrome to another is a big undertaking at best, but when the squadron uses state-of-the-art radar equipment and computers, moving is a tremendous challenge. The Snoopers had already made one move, from Henderson to Carney, but that move had been accomplished by trucks. The move to Munda not only had to be done by air; the support organizations of the 394th Bombardment Squadron had to be left behind and an airbase group was assigned to perform ground maintenance on the Snooper aircraft.

The runway was outstanding, but the living area was a mess. The average annual rainfall at Munda is 130 inches per year. Native lumber was available to floor the tents, but getting from the living quarters to working areas was messy. A handy hill that was pure coral had made the runway construction easy. The coral was also used to construct roads from the runway to the living area, but within the living area, there was usually ankle-deep muck. Areas near the runway had been paved with the coral carved out of the hill by the Seabee bulldozers for shops and working areas, and they were well drained and dry whenever the rain wasn't pelting down. The radar shop was located in a Quonset hut on one of the taxiways. Power was always a problem. Two motor-generator sets had to be kept running all the time. The main generator supplied 110-volt power for lights, tools, and of course the ever-present coffee pot. The other generator supplied twenty-eight volt power to run the flight equipment, which needed constant servicing and adjusting.

Master Sergeant Hune had used discarded bomb crates to construct a test stand that would hold a radar set with all the components in approximately the relative positions they were in the aircraft. He had located the test stand so the radar operator could look out the door of the Quonset hut and see small island targets across the bay on the east side of the runway. From the echoes he received from the islands, he had a fair test of the performance of the radar.

Technical Sergeant Shirey had done a similar job on a test stand for the computer, and Master Sergeant Hune and Technical Sergeant Shirey worked out together a scheme to feed the radar signals into the computer, much as it was done in the aircraft.

Bomb boxes were used for many things in the squadron. They were used because they were available in abundance. Most bombs were delivered to Munda by ship, and each bomb had to be crated so it could be stacked in the hold and not roll around. Once devoid of bombs, the crates were used to build cabinets in the shops and in the living quarters. They were used to build tables for the mess hall and they were used to build Ping-Pong tables, benches, and the bars in the officers' club and in the enlisted men's club. Sometimes it seemed that the war would come to a stop if there weren't enough bomb boxes, but of course the next ship would come in and the supply would be replenished.

The runway at Munda was outstanding for a number of reasons. First, it was hard and smooth; in fact, it was so smooth that the pilots commented that when they let the nose wheel down on landing it seemed that the B-24s picked up about ten miles per hour in their landing roll. The runway was 8,000 feet long and, being as hard and smooth as it was, it was a big improvement over most of the runways the Snoopers operated out of, which had been either soft and uneven or covered with metal Marston matting, which was noisy and slowed the airplanes down. The last 1,000 feet away from the ocean sloped up about ten feet. It was a challenge for the pilots to touch down at the ocean end of the runway, roll the whole 8,000 feet, and come to a stop at the top of the slope without touching the brakes.

Munda was the home of a type of frog that barked. In fact it was infested with them. They would get under the floorboards of our tents and bark all night long. They sounded just like small poodles, and just as loud, even though they were barely an inch long. The censors wouldn't let us mention them in our letters home, because New Georgia is apparently the only place in the world where they exist. The censors were afraid that if we told about the frogs, someone who was interested in zoology would figure out where we were. It was a big joke around the squadron because Tokyo Rose knew we were going to Munda even before we had been given the order to move.

In spite of the improved runway conditions, there were operational accidents at Munda. The Snoopers shared the base with a P-39 fighter squadron and other heavy bombardment squadrons would stage through Munda on their way to Rabaul. P-38 fighter squadrons would also stage through Munda. There seemed to be more operational accidents than were warranted.

One day a P-39 approached the runway with its wheels up. Technical Sergeant Shirey and two radar mechanics jumped in a jeep and rushed down the runway thinking that the fighter had been shot up and was in trouble—otherwise, why would the landing gear be retracted? They caught up with the P-39 just as it ground to a stop with the prop bent up, the bottom of the aircraft damaged, and the dust beginning to settle. The pilot threw back the canopy, stepped out onto the wing and said, "Goddammit, I forgot!"

On another occasion a P-38 landed and the nose gear collapsed. The aircraft slid on its nose for a while and then hooked a prop into the coral and flipped upside down with the pilot hanging by his harness. A Seabee ran out from the taxiway to the aircraft. Everyone who was watching thought he would help the pilot get out of his predicament. Not so. The Seabee kicked a piece of Plexiglas out of the canopy and ran, leaving the perplexed pilot still hanging by his harness. Seabee machinists were noted for the bracelets and other jewelry they constructed from Plexiglas. Where they got it didn't matter.

In the middle of a bright moonlit night a U.S. Navy PBY

(a version of the B-24) was lost, almost out of fuel, when the pilot saw the runway at Munda. On approach the pilot misjudged his altitude and impacted the water just short of the runway. The nose wheel was damaged and the ball turret (which was still down!) was damaged. Somehow the pilot managed to pull up enough to make it to the runway and grind to a stop with the nose of the PBY resting on the runway. The ball turret became detached and rolled down the runway ending up ahead of the PBY, with the gunner still in it! The crew later said that they thought they were on a Japanese runway, so they sat there with the engines running and all the gun turrets armed and ready to fire! Finally one of the airbase officers called to them and asked them what the hell they were doing and they tumbled to the fact that they were on a U.S. base instead of a Japanese base.

One Snooper crew was lost in an operational accident at Munda. First Lieutenant Richard Gay and crew were taking off in one of the original Snooper aircraft; two engines lost power at a critical time in the climb-out and Lieutenant Gay was forced to land in the water. There were three survivors: Lieutenant Jack Toole, the copilot; Staff Sergeant LaMica, the flight engineer; and Technical Sergeant Dyer, the radar operator. This accident was the first of several that plagued the Snoopers due to the heavy loads that they were forced to carry and the very long missions that they were assigned. The engines were required to produce much more than specified power on take off and they would fail at times that made it impossible for the pilots to recover control.

By early 1944 the Japanese were frantically trying to re-supply their troops on many of the islands in the Solomons and in the vicinity of Rabaul. The Snoopers had so devastated their capital ships that the Japanese had turned to small coastal vessels, known as Sugar-Charlies, to transport supplies. They also did their best to camouflage them so they would look like small islands. Foliage was draped across the rigging, the paint was mottled and bright green. To prevent surveillance aircraft from spotting them, they would stop moving when they saw or heard an aircraft in their vicinity. That ploy fooled most of the surveillance aircraft, but it didn't fool the Snooper radar operators. They could spot the Sugar-Charlies from twenty or thirty miles and see them move before the Sugar-Charlies knew the Snooper was there.

It was one thing to find the Sugar-Charlies, but it was another matter to sink them. When the radar and computer was used to drop bombs on them, the results were poor. Bombardiers had a hard time keeping the computers tracking on the relatively weak signal that returned from the Sugar-Charlies, and dropping from fifteen hundred feet on the small targets resulted in a lot of misses. Many of the bombardiers became frustrated because they had gone on several missions and, although they had seen Sugar-Charlies on almost every mission, they had not been able to get direct hits or confirmed sinkings.

It was a surprise to everyone in the Snooper squadron when one of the replacement crew members, pilot Lt. Phillip Hoffman, reported three Sugar-Charlies sunk on the crew's second mission. All of the bombardiers were anxious to find out how bombardier Gene Maggioncalda had done it.

Gene said that after his first mission (on which he'd had no success) he convinced Lieutenant Hoffman that they would have more chance for success if they changed the way they attacked the Sugar-Charlies. Instead of going in at 1,000 or 1,500 feet to allow the radar operator the best chance of seeing and identifying the Sugar-Charlies, then when they located one, Lieutenant Hoffman would head for the ship and lose altitude until they were 200 feet above the water about five miles from the ship and plan to cross over the top of the ship at 200 mph and 200 feet altitude. Lieutenant Maggioncalda set the Norden bombsight at a drop angle of seventy degrees to the vertical. As they approached the ship, Lieutenant Maggioncalda gave the pilot steering directions over the intercom; when the waterline of the ship touched the horizontal cross-hair on the Norden, he toggled out two bombs as fast as he could. One hit the water line and the second landed on the deck. It was necessary for him to change the fusing on the bombs to five-second delay instead of the two-tenths second delay that was used for bombing with the computer. This was a change that could be made in flight. It worked! Within a few days, almost every bombardier in the squadron had been credited with one or more sinkings of the ubiquitous Sugar-Charlies.

April 1944

The Japanese pulled all of their remaining aircraft that were in flyable condition out of Rabaul by the end of February 1944. The Snoopers had been so successful in preventing the Japanese from supplying their troops that they had decided to pull back and make a stand at Truk Island. General MacArthur's successful invasion of Los Negros Island in the Admiralty group and the subsequent capture of Momote airfield gave Maj. Gen. Hubert Harmon, who had taken command of the Thirteenth Air Force, the opportunity to station the Snoopers nearer to Truk and the center of Japanese resistance. The Snoopers were on the move again by the end of April 1944 and relocated at Momote.

The Admiralty Islands

Small, crescent-shaped Los Negros Island in the Admiralty group, which is the most northerly of the Melanesian Islands, lies but two degrees south of the equator. Los Negros was practically unheard of before World War II. With the enemy in control of islands not far away, Los Negros assumed a new importance. Strategically situated, in a position to control the Bismarck Sea and the approaches Rabaul, within Liberator-range of key Japanese bases in the Carolines and New Guinea, Los Negros was of great military value.

The Japanese had recognized this early in the war and had built an airstrip on the southeastern corner of the island. Although not a large field, it was used by the Japanese to support their defense of Rabaul and New Guinea. Near the end of 1943, it was vulnerable to attack by the Fifth Air Force; by March 1944, its effectiveness as a Japanese base was neutralized.

Early in February, plans were completed by General MacArthur to seize the Admiralties on 1 April, 1944, by a combined operation. Major provisions of this plan provided for: 1) the seizure of Kavieng by South Pacific Forces, thus neutralizing Japanese defensive strength in the New Ireland—New Britain area; 2) the invasion of Los Negros by the Sixth Army, supported by the Allied air and naval forces; 3) the continued pressure by the New Guinea force against the enemy in the Ramu River Valley and along the New Guinea coast; 4) and the cooperation of Central Pacific forces by virtue of their continued pressure against the Japanese in the Carolines to the north.

A number of circumstances led General MacArthur's Supreme Headquarters to change the date for the invasion of the Admiralties from April 1 to February 29. The Japanese were found to be unexpectedly weak in the central Pacific; they were unable to resist the Navy's successful carrier strike against Truk on February 16 and 17. There was an unexpected decrease in Japanese air strength at Rabaul in the middle of February. Thus there seemed to be signs that the Japanese were abandoning the fight in the South Pacific; these were supported by the fact that intensive reconnaissance of the Admiralties failed to show any Japanese activity there. For the above reasons, along with the desire to press forward the offensive, and to keep pace with the Navy's drive in the Central Pacific, General MacArthur decided to advance D-day to the last day in February.

The ability of the Japanese to keep their installations concealed was not overlooked. While the intent was to capture and seize Los Negros, a retirement was planned in case the enemy showed unexpected strength. Another Tarawa was to be avoided. The Fifth Cavalry Regiment of the First Cavalry Division, which later led the march into Tokyo, landed on schedule on February 29, and in one hour and thirty-five minutes captured Momote Airdrome against weak opposition. Their initial success led General MacArthur to decide to seize all the islands in the Admiralty group, which was the original purpose of the action. It was not long, however, before the small garrison on Los Negros was reinforced from Manus Island. A sharp struggle took place against mounting opposition, which was successfully met by throwing into the fight the resources of the First Division, which had arrived on Los Negros in its entirety.

Momote proved to be at best only an average airdrome. It had to be improved both with regard to the length of the runway and the size of the revetment areas. The runway was not level; there was a gentle slope from each end to a rise of several feet in the middle. This caused many operational accidents on takeoff, especially for pilots who had not flown off of Momote before. After passing the hump in the middle of the runway, pilots received the sensation that they were airborne when, in fact, they did not have sufficient airspeed to begin flying. They would call for "wheels up" and then settle back into the ground with disastrous results. This difficulty was never corrected because it would have required the runway to be closed for several weeks to make the required changes; the field was too badly needed to permit closing it down for so long a period of time.

Los Negros with its coral base was an ideal island for airstrips. Soon after the First Cavalry Division had cleared the island of Japanese defenders, Army and Navy engineers went to work on a second airfield at Mokerang Plantation on the northern tip of the crescent. By mid-April one strip at Mokerang was rapidly nearing completion and work on a second strip had begun. Working around the clock, with two giant antiaircraft searchlights serving as floodlights for the night shift, the 821st Engineer Aviation Battalion had the 8,000-foot runway ready for use on May 26.

Welcome Home, Snooper

Six hundred . . . five-fifty . . . five twenty-five . . . five hundred; level her off." Copilot Charles Beatty called off altitude as he and Tom Arthur rapidly descended to protect the vulnerable belly of their B-24.

"Roy, what's the situation back there?" This was a query by pilot Tom Arthur to the tail turret gunner, Staff Sergeant Roy Westberg.

"We still have three Zeros following us, Lieutenant; I think they thought we were going into the drink, but now they are in a loose line behind us and it looks like they will be making strafing runs on us."

"Give them a burst if they start to make a pass."

"Roger," said Roy, almost nonchalantly.

The Arthur crew had been on a ship-search mission and had sunk a Japanese cargo ship, but it was late in the mission, and as they were turning for home, Mokerang, with the sun coming up, five Zeros suddenly appeared out of nowhere and jumped them.

Lieutenant Arthur and his crew were Snoopers. They were flying B-24s that had been given major modifications to allow nighttime bombing of ships. One of the modification was to replace the ball turret in the belly of the B-24 with radar, so they were very vulnerable from below. That was why they had made a sudden dive after the first surprise attack of the Zeros.

"Skipper, those Zeros have floats," said Staff Sergeant Westberg.

"You mean they're float planes?"

"Roger, here they come!"

The attack was completely uncoordinated. Each of the Zeros made an independent run on the Snooper. As each one came within firing range, Roy gave him a burst with his twin fifty-caliber machine guns, and he could see hits. He knew that the Zeros used 7.7-mm machine guns to test the range and windage before firing their twenty-mm cannons, so he would wait until he saw 7.7s come close and then return a burst with his fifties. Since Ray was firing downwind, his fire was much more effective than the fire from the Zeros.

Lieutenant Arthur was counting on the Zeros having limited range and hoping that they would have to return to base before they had inflicted any serious damage to the B-24. Staff Sergeant Quinn Hess was manning the top turret. Between Roy and Quinn, the Zeros took more damage than they handed out. It was apparent that their pilots were not the dedicated, well-trained breed who had been so aggressive earlier in the war. Aggressive or not, they had managed to put seven 7.7 holes in the B-24.

"They're turning back!" Roy sang out. "One is landing in the water; I think I saw some hits on his engine a while ago."

"Keep a sharp eye out for more of those bandits," warned Lieutenant Arthur. "We have to go by more Jap-controlled islands on the way home, and they could have been warning that we are out here all by ourselves."

"Ben, pull that radome up as far as you can and still get land targets." Sgt. Ben Myers was the radar operator and he knew that the fiberglass radome over the radar antenna created extra drag on the aircraft, and now it was more important to have extra speed and endurance than to have the full capability of the radar. He cranked the radome up until just the lower part of the hemisphere was extended below the belly of the B-24; in this position, the radome offered very little extra drag, but enough of the antenna was below the bottom surface of the aircraft to allow him to see island targets. That way they could navigate their way home to Mokerang at full speed, and they were all anxious to report the ship sinking and the presence of the float-plane Zeros to squadron headquarters.

It was March 1944, and the Snoopers had been remarkably successful in stopping the Japanese from resupplying their Pacific outposts. The B-24s could range over 1,000 miles from their home bases and each airplane could search 500,000 square miles per hour. Any ship that moved in the enormous areas of the search patterns was certain to be sunk. The radar would find them and the airborne computer would use the radar signals to put bombs right under the keel of any ship sighted.

Lieutenant Arthur and his crew had searched long and hard to find the ship that they finally attacked. It was not only late in the night, but it was near the end of endurance for the B-24. The bombardier, Lieutenant Ray Mallette, had dropped the whole load of bombs in one "stick" on the cargo ship, because he would have had to dump them anyway to lighten the aircraft so they could make it home before the fuel ran out. The fighter attack just made it worse. Running at higher than cruise speed and taking evasive action used up more of the precious fuel than they could comfortably afford.

"Wayne, how does our fuel supply look?" Lieutenant Arthur asked the navigator, Wayne Plummer.

"I estimate that we will have about 100 gallons left when we touch down, Tom, so don't make any pattern maneuvers, just ask for a straight-in approach."

With the radome retracted and the aircraft virtually empty of bomb-load and fuel, they were flying at an airspeed of 180 knots, but Lieutenant Plummer asked Lieutenant Arthur to reduce power to save fuel. Normal power setting for cruise on the B-24 was 2,000 rpm and thirty inches of mercury manifold pressure. This would result in 160 knots airspeed with a normal load. With the lightly loaded plane, Lieutenant Arthur pulled the manifold pressure back to twenty-five inches and the rpm to 1,800. They were still making 160 knots but the fuel usage was significantly reduced.

"Wayne, what is our ETA at Mokerang?"

"I make it 10:05 local, Tom."

"You mean we have two more hours to go? How is the gas holding out?"

"An hour and fifty minutes, Tom, and the gas is a little worse than I thought. That's why I asked you to reduce power."

"Well, okay, Wayne, but keep me posted. I want some warning if I have to ditch."

"Roger."

Sometimes a minute can seem like an hour, but when the gas gauge is inching down toward empty and there are a few hundred miles of ocean between you and the nearest friendly runway, an hour can seem like a lifetime. Wayne made minor course corrections to account for wind shifts; he noted that they had a quartering tail wind that helped, and the reduced engine power was helping, but it was still going to be touch-and-go.

Lieutenant Arthur had trimmed the B-24 so that they would climb very gradually, and by the time they were thirty minutes from Mokerang, they were at 6,000 feet altitude; Ben could see the island on the radar.

"Radar to navigator: Mokerang is at eighty miles range, twelve o'clock. The BUPS beacon is on the scope." (The BUPS beacon was an experimental location aid for the Snoopers that was set up at each of their operating bases. It showed up as a bright dot on the radar scope and was easily distinguished from land targets. It was usually located near the end of the operating runway and in bad weather it could even be used as an aid to landing approach.)

"Mokerang tower, this is army 961, request straight-in. I'm going to be on fumes," said Lieutenant Arthur.

"Army 961, give me your present position and put your IFF on code C."

"Roger, Mokerang. Seventy-five-northwest of the BUPS beacon. IFF is on code C." (The IFF was a piece of electronic gear that was carried on every U.S. aircraft and the aircraft of U.S. allies. It identified each aircraft as friendly to the search radar and to antiaircraft radar.)

"Army 961, give me five minutes warning of your position ten miles from touchdown."

"Roger."

Twenty minutes crept by at a snail's pace.

"Mokerang. This is *961,* five minutes to the ten-mile mark."

"Roger, *961.* You are clear to make a straight-in approach."

"Roger."

Now it was eight minutes to touchdown. There was no gas showing in the sight gauges. Lieutenant Arthur began to descend and reduced power to conserve what little gas was left. He passed the ten-mile mark at 2,500 feet and reduced power again to reach sea-level altitude just as he reached the end of the runway.

"Mokerang, this is *961,* I'm three miles from touchdown."

"Roger, *961,* the wind is fifteen knots from the south."

"Roger, Mokerang."

Now it was necessary to put the B-24 into landing configuration: Wheels down, half flaps and engine power up to compensate for the extra drag. The engine mixture controls had to go to full rich, which caused the engines to gobble what little gas was left.

Over the end of the runway, engine number one sputtered and quit. "It had to be number one," muttered copilot Beatty, as he helped Lieutenant Arthur kick the heavy right rudder and turn the right aileron. Losing the flow from the number one engine caused the left wing to dip and the aircraft to yaw dangerously to the left.

"I knew it would be number one, Chuck. That right cross wind caused it." Lieutenant Arthur had to fly with the right wing low because of the right cross wind and the result was that the fuel pump in the left engine was uncovered first.

Together Lieutenant Arthur and Lieutenant Beatty got the aircraft under control and set it down, none too gently, but safely, on the runway, a feat that was not helped a bit by the windmilling number one engine, which hadn't had time to respond to the feathering button.

"Mokerang tower, this is army *961,* we are on the ground. I don't think we have enough gas to taxi to the revetment area."

"Roger, *961.* A cletrack is on the way. Welcome home."

Gekko

Just before and during WWII, United States and British military considered radar to be so classified that even the word "radar" was kept under security wraps. The British "chain radar" was credited with a major part of the defense of England during the air raids of 1940–45. Germany obtained enough of the technology from agents in England, that they had developed the Wurtzburg antiaircraft gun-directing radar and the surveillance radar that fed data to the Wurtzburg radar by the end of 1943, but information on radar technology was slow to arrive in Japan. As a result, the Snoopers were seldom detected by their targets until it was too late. Flying in cloudy weather or at night, they would approach blacked-out ships, whose crews probably felt perfectly safe from attack, and deliver devastating blows, which resulted in almost instantaneous sinkings.

Even at the end of the conflict, in 1945, the Japanese Armed Forces were still without the detection and gun-laying capability of the United States Navy and Air forces.

If they were handicapped on the ground from lack of radar warning systems and antiaircraft directing systems, they were completely devoid of airborne radars. Even before WWII began, the United States and Britain had airborne sea-search radar, which they called ASV (air to surface vessel), and night-fighter radar, which they called AI (aircraft intercept), but the Japanese had no equivalent systems. It almost seemed to air crews who fought against the Japanese air crews that they did not even use two-way radio in their fighter aircraft. From observations of tactics, it appeared that there was one airborne radio transmitter in the aircraft of the squadron commander, and the rest of the squadron only had receivers. This situation often resulted in the squadron being disorganized when the squadron commander's plane was shot down.

It was quite noticeable during nighttime harassing missions over Japanese-held bases in the Solomon Islands, during 1942 and 1943, that the Japanese defense forces would throw up inaccurate antiaircraft fire and there was no attempt on their part to fly night-fighter missions.

Rabaul was a major stronghold of the Japanese north of Australia, so it was necessary to neutralize it. Daily air raids were made on Rabaul during 1943 and 1944, and the nighttime harassing missions were flown every night to keep the fighter pilots awake, and therefore less alert when they were defending Rabaul from the United States heavy bombers and fighters and the Australian and New Zealand fighters during the day. By 1944, the Japanese shipping had been so decimated by the Snoopers that their missions were often void of ship contacts and their bomb loads would go to secondary targets. Brigadier General Matheny considered these fruitless ship-search missions to be less important than the harassing missions, so the Snoopers, who were trained to fly at night and in bad weather, and who had the airborne radar to get them to the targets no matter what the visibility, were assigned many of the harassing missions over Rabaul.

In 1943, the harassing missions were similar to the harassing missions that had been carried out in the Solomons, but early in 1944, something deadly appeared. The first indication was the appearance of a very bright blue searchlight. It was directed by a sensor that was a primitive form of radar.

It did not hunt around the sky for the harassing aircraft; when it touched the aircraft it was illuminated and the light clung like a leach. No amount of maneuvering would shake it. And with it came Gekko.

Gekko was a twin-engine fighter, very similar to the U.S. Air Force P-38. It had a high rate of climb and was very maneuverable. Aerial photographs had spotted it in revetments areas at Rabaul, and U.S. Intelligence had given it the code name of Irving.

The Gekko had been designed by Nakajima to compensate for some of the shortcomings of the Mark 0 Zero fighter and the more advanced Mark II Zero. They could both be outmaneuvered by the US P-38 at high altitudes, and Gekko was designed to remedy that void in Japanese fighter capability. Because the design was started so late in the war, very few Gekkos were delivered to combat. One was delivered to Rabaul and another was delivered to Truk Atoll, a major Japanese naval stronghold in the Caroline islands Gekko's pilot was a military test pilot who delivered the aircraft to Rabaul and who flew several missions against the U.S. heavy bombers on daylight missions. The Japanese defense forces at Rabaul had been searching for an aircraft that could be used to fly against the nighttime harassing missions, and the Gekko seemed to fill this need.

The blue searchlight had been developed after feverish work in Japan by Dr. Hidetsugu Yagi and his staff at the Tokyo Institute of Technology. (Dr. Yagi had invented the Yagi antenna in 1928, the type of antenna that is seen on almost every house in America today as a TV antenna.) It used radio signals and an array of Yagi antennas to direct the searchlight which would allow the optical trackers to work at night, and the crews who flew the harassing missions reported that with the appearance of the blue searchlight, the antiaircraft fire seemed to be more accurate than it had been previously. They also reported that often the antiaircraft fire would stop at unusual times. Normally antiaircraft fire was most intense when the bomb run was being made. During a bomb run, the aircraft had to be flown in a fairly straight line to allow the bombardier to aim the bombsight, and it was then that the antiaircraft batteries could make the best predictions of where to aim the shells so they would burst close to the aircraft. That wasn't always happening at Rabaul, and the reason became apparent when one of the crews on a harassing mission was fired on by a Gekko.

The pilot of the Gekko was Lieutenant Tadashi Minobe.

He had tested the new fighter at the Nakajima factory and was impressed with its speed, its maneuverability at high altitudes, with a full load of fuel and ammunition. It was equipped with two 7.7-mm machine guns and four twenty-mm cannons, all firing forward. Lieutenant Minobe recognized a shortcoming with the aircraft configuration during that first attempt to shoot down the harassing B-24 over Rabaul. To keep the B-24 in sight after it was spotted by the blue searchlight, Lieutenant Minobe had to fly several thousand feet below and somewhat behind the big bomber. As he poured on power and approached the bomber from below, his aircraft would fly out in front of the bomber and he couldn't aim properly. He finally fired at a B-24 in April 1944 with little success. The bullets flew in front of the bomber and the crew immediately took evasive action and escaped, shaken up but unharmed.

Lieutenant Minobe returned to Rabaul and instructed the armament organization to refit the Gekko with four twenty-mm cannons that fired up through the gun compartment at a sixty-degree angle with the line of flight. He also refitted the gunsight so that it looked up at that same sixty-degree angle. Now he had a night fighter that was able to find the night-flying bombers when they were in the blue searchlight, and when he poured on power and came up underneath them, he was not only in perfect position to see them in his gunsight, but he was also firing at the largest area that the bomber could project—the total wing area and the whole bottom area of the fuselage. Lieutenant Minobe was quick to use the newly outfitted Gekko, and by mid-April 1944, just ten days after the modifications, he shot down a B-24 on a night harassing mission over Rabaul. He quickly informed Warrant Officer Yoshimasa Nakagawa at Truk Atoll of the modifications. The Gekko at Truk was immediately modified and ready for action.

Close Call

April 1944

Number one engine was missing intermittently. It would run smooth as glass for an hour, and then without warning it would cut out three or four times. It wasn't enough that they were out on a black-dark night, and had just ridden through a tropical front; now they were going to bomb the islands in Truk Lagoon with an engine acting up.

"Pilot to navigator: What's our ETA to the target?"

"I can see it on the radar, Don, sixty miles dead ahead. We should be on the bombing run in twenty minutes."

"Pilot to crew: Everybody be on the lookout and if you see that new night fighter, sing out."

"Navigator to radar: Give me a sector scan, thirty degrees at twelve o'clock."

"Radar. Roger."

Fifteen minutes dragged by. The crew members' nerves were tight as wires. Truk was heavily defended with antiaircraft weapons. The Japanese evidently had an effective antiaircraft radar, which directed a bright blue searchlight that would be full on the aircraft when it lit up, and recently there were rumors of a new night fighter that had given several of the night harassing mission crews nasty surprises. Lt. Don Thompson and crew were less than anxious to tangle with either the antiaircraft fire or the night fighter, but they were determined to complete the mission, sick engine or not. They were Snoopers.

"Navigator to pilot: IP in one minute."

The big blue searchlight came on and hung on the aircraft like a leach. Thirty seconds later, antiaircraft shells began bursting around them.

"Pilot to bombardier: Parson, you got it."

"Roger, Don. I'll drop in about thirty seconds."

The bombardier, Lt. Nick Milos, nicknamed the Parson, tried to ignore the antiaircraft shells that began bursting around the B-24 with angry *crumps*. Thirty seconds seems like a long time with *crump, crump, crump* shaking the plane every second.

"Bombs away," sang out the Parson. Almost instantly the antiaircraft fire stopped. The big blue searchlight was still on. It didn't hunt around; it just stayed with them. As soon as the bombs were away, Lieutenant Thompson took evasive action, but nothing would shake that blue searchlight.

"Bandit at six o'clock, low," came over the intercom from the tail gunner, Sgt. Shorty Fletcher. "He's coming up under us. I can't aim that low!"

Because of the unarmed belly of the Snooper B-24, they were very vulnerable to attack from below. In spite of wild evasive maneuvers by Lieutenant Thompson, they were still in the big blue searchlight, and during the steep banks, the waist gunners could see the night fighter climbing up under them.

Suddenly, the number one engine missed. It missed as though the ignition had been cut for two full seconds, then it came back on as suddenly as it had gone off. A ball of fire twenty feet in diameter came out of the exhaust stack and the whole airplane shook with the force of the explosion.

"He's turning off!" shouted the right waist gunner.

"The searchlight is wandering off," reported Shorty, after another minute had passed. "We must be getting out of range of their radar."

Nobody was relaxing. They still didn't know if the night fighter had an airborne radar or if he relied solely on the search-light.

Ten tense minutes went by.

"Pilot to crew: I think we are out of range of that night fighter. All stations report."

"Navigator, here. Come to a course of 180 so I can lay a course to base."

"Pilot to navigator: Roger, one eighty."

"Bombardier to pilot: Bombs were right on target, Don."

"Radar on and operating."

"Waist Gunner. Still here."

"Tail Gunner. Okay."

It was relax-and-get-rid-of-tension time.

"Pilot to crew: That night-fighter pilot must have thought we were shooting at him with sixteen-inch guns."

"Waist to pilot: He sure didn't stick around after that backfire."

"Pilot to navigator: Give me a course to base."

"Navigator to pilot: You are doing pretty well, Don. Stick to 180 for a while. We still have that front to tippy-toe through in about an hour."

Number one ran smoothly all the way back to Mokerang.

A Nasty Surprise

Late April 1944

The runway at Mokerang was coral. Some of it had been scraped clean and left, but some of the runway had been made from coral that was dug out and filled and then rolled. When it was dry, it was a good primitive runway, but when it was wet, which was most of the time, it was "slow." It would soften up and add over a thousand feet to the takeoff run of the badly overloaded Snooper B-24s. The Snooper aircraft were over-loaded for a number of reasons. First, they carried the radar and computer that made it possible for them to bomb ships out of a dark night or cloudy weather. Second, their missions were duration limited; that is, they flew as long as the aircraft had gas to fly. Most missions were flown with full wing tanks, wing-tip tanks and from one to three bomb bays filled with auxiliary tanks. The result of these configurations was that a "normal" Snooper mission would begin with a B-24 that was 10,000 to 15,000 pounds over the maximum gross weight specified for that type of aircraft.

Lieutenant Tom Arthur and crew were assigned to a harassing mission over Truk Island. Because the object of the mission was to keep the defenders awake as long as possible, their aircraft, *Libby Raider,* was fitted with three bomb-bay fuel tanks, and ten 100-pound general purpose bombs were loaded into the fourth bomb bay. With bombs, extra fuel, radar, computer, and armament, *Libby Raider* weighed in at just under

70,000 pounds gross, a staggering load for an airplane that was designed to fly with a maximum gross weight of 56,000 pounds.

It was a soggy afternoon. The rain had been light and intermittent all afternoon. The runway had many slight depressions that held from one-half to an inch of water (that was about as level as the engineers could get it with bulldozers and rollers). In addition to the standing water, there was a soft spot at the south end of the runway that just seemed to drag at the airplane interminably. Eight thousand feet of runway sounds like a lot for a B-24, but with all the handicaps added up, *Libby* reluctantly came off the ground as she reached the over-run area. Lieutenant Arthur trimmed back slightly and asked Lieutenant Beatty for "wheels up." Getting rid of the drag of the landing gear helped, but it was almost two more long minutes before they had enough altitude to gradually ease up the flaps and set their course for Truk.

"Wayne, give a heading," Lieutenant Arthur asked of Lieutenant Plummer.

"Take five degrees magnetic, Tom," replied Lieutenant Plummer, "We're going to have to weave our way through this stormy weather."

"Roger, Wayne. Take us through the soft spots."

With *Libby* loaded as she was, 140 knots was the best Lieutenant Arthur could coax out of her for the first hour. At the end of the first hour *Libby* had used almost 2,000 pounds of gasoline and although still overloaded, she was beginning to fly more like an airplane. The weather was no help. Ben Myers had cranked the radome part way down as soon as the wheels and flaps were up and Lieutenant Plummer could see the thunderheads swirling around them. He picked out the lightest spots that were more or less on course for Truk.

"Tom, we are about out of this front. Take a course of ten degrees magnetic and hold it until we hit the next one in about two hours."

"Roger, Wayne, that was a good job of tippy-toeing through that last one."

Warrant Officer Nakagawa was on alert. He had been on

alert every night for almost a month; not only that, the almost daily bombing raids of the islands in Truk lagoon by the Fifth and 307th groups of the Thirteenth Air Force had left him tired and jittery. He was always fearful that his Gekko would be damaged by the almost saturation bombing from the B-24s.

The Gekko had worked well during the several missions that he had flown at night during the month of April and, with the modifications that had been made at Lieutenant Minobe's direction, Nakagawa was sure that he would soon get a kill.

Every day after the heavy bombers had made their bombing run and departed, he would carefully go over every inch of his Gekko. Engine checks, fueling, armament checks were all done with religious attention to detail. Warrant Officer Nakagawa always fired a burst from the four twenty-mm cannons that stuck up through the fuselage, and it always attracted attention of other personnel who were mystified by the twenty-mm cannon shells that arced up over the beach and fell several hundred yards out in the lagoon. Often when Nakagawa climbed down from his Gekko one of the mechanics from an adjoining revetment or one of the island staff would say to him jokingly, "Warrant Officer Nakagawa, do you expect to shoot down enemy planes while your airplane is still on the ground?" And Warrant Officer Nakagawa would reply, "The enemy I shoot at will be more surprised than you!"

Although the Japanese did not have radar to detect incoming aircraft, they did have sensitive listening devices. The day bombers and the night harassing missions all came from the same direction, almost due south, so the listening devices were positioned to pick up the sound of engines as soon as they came over the horizon. This gave the day fighters more than an hour of warning. A group of forty B-24s in formation made such a roar that the listener on the audio detector could hear them 200 miles away. This gave the day fighters plenty of time to start engines, take off, climb to intercept altitude and be in position to attack when the bombers were on their bombing runs.

Gekko's mission timing was not so liberal. The single B-24

made much less noise than a whole group, so Warrant Officer Nakagawa often had only a half hour warning of the approach of the harassing aircraft. Such was the case that night. It was almost midnight when the alert sounded and Warrant Officer Nakagawa climbed into the cockpit of Gekko and started the engines. The whole Truk Atoll was under blackout conditions, so the runway lights that were available to Warrant Officer Nakagawa were like a row of fireflies on each side of the runway. The runway had only been marginally repaired from the bombing raid of the day; the takeoff run was a nightmare. Once off the ground, Gekko flew beautifully, and Warrant Officer Nakagawa headed south and climbed for altitude.

All of the night harassing missions for the month of April had flown at 15,000 feet altitude, so Warrant Officer Nakagawa climbed to 10,000 and zigzagged back and forth across a line due south from the atoll. The sensor for the blue searchlight caught the B-24 while it was still seven miles south of Truk, and Warrant Officer Nakagawa was surprised to see that it was only a couple of thousand feet above him. He stayed well behind the B-24 while the antiaircraft fire was coming up from the ground, then when the antiaircraft shells stopped exploding, he opened the throttles and quickly caught up with the B-24. This was the first time he had tried to use the new gunsight at night and he had to jockey several times until he had the big B-24 in the sight and had controlled the rate of climb properly.

The second front that Lieutenant Arthur had to fly through was every bit as nasty as the front they had gone through just north of Mokerang. It was rougher riding for all of the crew because they had been climbing to bombing altitude, which was 12,000 feet, and the storms were much more turbulent at that altitude than they had been at the low altitude they had been at when they went through the first one. They broke out 200 miles south of Truk and the ride became smoother. The sky cleared up too, and they could see stars everywhere.

"Wayne, you can brush up on your celestial [navigation]!" Lieutenant Arthur kidded Lieutenant Plummer. "You navigate by the radar so much you're probably rusty."

"Don't worry, Tom. I've been keeping a DR [dead reckoning] fix. I estimate we will see Truk dead ahead on the radar within ten minutes."

It was time for the gunners to get on station and charge their fifty-caliber machine guns. Lieutenant Mallette, the bombardier, set his intervalometer for the first run they had planned and activated the Norden bombsight, just in case he could get a visual sighting of one of the islands in the lagoon. He rechecked the slant range calculations for a radar drop, in the more likely case that he would have to drop on the radar signals.

"Truk at twelve o'clock, 120 miles," Sgt. Ray Myers sang out over the intercom.

"Okay, I was a minute off," Lieutenant Plummer replied.

"All hands report," said Lieutenant Arthur.

"Nose Turret, ready."

"Top Turret, ready."

"Waist Guns, ready."

"Tail Turret, ready."

"Radar on and operating."

"Bombardier, ready."

"Navigator, ready. We should be at IP [initiation point of the bomb run] in ten minutes. Hold the present course."

Two minutes before the IP the searchlight had come on. There was no hunting around—it had just popped on and they were in the light. Thirty seconds later, the antiaircraft shells began bursting, but they only lasted about a minute and then they stopped. The only sound was the drone of the engines.

"Bomb-bay doors opening," said Lieutenant Mallette.

"Verify doors open," said Lieutenant Plummer.

"*Tom!* We've got a fighter under us!" Lieutenant Plummer screamed.

The warning came too late. The first burst of Gekko's four twenty-mm cannons came right in through the open bomb bay. Three fuel cells filled with fumes and holding twenty five gallons of residual 100-octane gasoline burst with an explosion that tore the B-24 into two pieces just behind the wing, and the G forces made it impossible for the crew to escape from their doomed aircraft. The G forces also buckled the wings of the B-24, ruptured the wing tanks, and added to the fierce conflagration.

Warrant Officer Nakagawa cut power to the Gekko's engines and rolled rapidly to the left to escape the debris that rained down from the stricken B-24. He broke radio silence to report the destruction of the B-24 and asked for runway lights. He was anxious to get back to Truk and report the success of Gekko as a night fighter. He was also eager to communicate with Lieutenant Minobe to congratulate him on the modification to Gekko that had made the mission a success.

Getting back to Truk was not all that easy. He had to rely on radio direction finding to give him a course to the airfield and then the little runway lights and the rough runway were severe challenges. He was tempted to make a victory roll over the runway before he touched down, but that maneuver on a black-dark night would be foolhardy and, besides, nobody on the ground would see it anyway. He did make one low pass over the runway to be sure that he would see the runway lights when he was on final approach. After the pass, Warrant Officer Nakagawa made a long low approach and touched down easily, then rolled to a bumpy stop at the end of the runway. Wing tip walkers helped him taxi to his revetment area where he cut his engines and climbed down to a rousing welcome.

The Joker Arrives

"Mokerang Tower, this is aircraft *923*, request approach clearance."

"Roger, *923*. You are ahead of your ETA. Switch your IFF to code C and give me an estimate of your fuel remaining."

"Roger, Mokerang. IFF is on C. I have one hour and five minutes fuel remaining."

"Roger, *923*. Look for the BUPS beacon and establish a ten-minute racetrack at angels five, fifty miles northeast of BUPS."

"Roger. Willco," replied 2nd Lt. Jack Wagner, then said to the crew on the intercom, "Looks like we have some time to waste, guys. We could have stayed in the Red Dog game at Carney a little longer."

Wagner and crew were fresh out of combat training at Fairfield-Suisan, which they had left on March 21, 1944, and they were replacements for a crew of the 868th Bombardment Squadron H, known throughout the Thirteenth Air Force as the Snoopers.

923 had arrived early because Wagner and crew were eager to move from the daylight-training missions they had been flying since joining the Thirteenth, Air Force. They were ready to start flying combat missions in earnest.

The delay of their arrival at Mokerang was due to the return of the 307th Bomb Group from a daylight mission to Truk Atoll. Truk was a mid-Pacific stronghold of the Japanese military and naval forces. Although it was effectively neutralized by the planes of the Seventh and Thirteenth Air Forces and the ships of NAVPAC, it was heavily defended by the best Japanese fighter aircraft and was a refueling and resupply base for the Japanese submarine fleet. It was the key to the Japanese inner defense of the homeland. Because of its strategic importance to the defense of Japan, it was fanatically defended. The 307th Group had flown their B-24s more than 2,000 miles, through two intense tropical fronts, and had been met by more than 100 Japanese Mark II Zeros. Wagner and crew had to stand by for aircraft that were critically short on fuel. Many were badly damaged and several carried wounded or dead crew members. It took forty-five minutes to get them all down, and Lieutenant Wagner was beginning to get concerned about his own fuel supply when his radio erupted.

"*923,* you are cleared for an approach to Mokerang. Left-hand pattern on runway 1-2."

"Roger, Mokerang, we're on our way."

The approach was uneventful. The BUPS beacon was near the end of the main runway, so Wagner lined it up at 120 degrees.

The radar operator reported ten miles range. "Mokerang, this is *923.* Ten miles from 1-2. We have the runway in sight."

"Roger, *923,*" said Mokerang Tower. "The follow-me jeep is waiting for you at the south end of the runway."

923 was nicknamed "The Joker" by Wagner's crew. Painted under the name was a beautiful brunette in a black and red body stocking wearing cap and bells. The airplane was the newest Snooper-configured B-24. The most noticeable difference from the original Snooper B-24s that Wagner parked in line with was the nose turret. All of the original Snooper aircraft had the greenhouse in the nose. Original Snoopers only mounted one fifty-caliber machine gun in the nose and had no armor plate.

Wagner and crew were met by a carryall that took them to the 868th camp area. All of the living and working quarters were either pyramidal tents or Quonset huts. The Officer-of-the-Day welcomed them and showed them their new quarters.

"Tell room service I have some laundry to go out, and I need a bucket of ice." Lieutenant Goerke was always trying to make light of a dismal situation. The tents sagged; they were set on bare dirt; and with four men to a tent, there was no such thing as privacy. The crew was used to primitive living, having staged through Buttons, New Hebrides, and Carney, Guadalcanal, but the realization that this was a semipermanent home, even more dismal than their recent temporary quarters, was enough to depress everyone's spirits, even those of the usually jovial Goerke.

Before dark settled in, the commanding officer of the 868th, Maj. Jim Barlow, dropped by to welcome them. Jim was a very amiable CO; he tried to make up for the fact that he was not one of the original Snoopers by being helpful and easy to get along with. He had been assigned as CO of the 868th from the Forty-third Group, which was a group of B-25, Michell medium bombers. He had flown his twenty five missions with the Forty-third and he did not feel comfortable flying Snooper missions. Whenever he made his welcoming call on a new crew, he always managed to work in a story about when he was flying for the movie *A Guy Named Joe*. He looked so much like Spencer Tracy that he had been selected over a long list of other B-25 pilots to fly some of the film sequences and he was proud of it. As part of his welcome, Major Barlow reviewed the role that the Snoopers had had in eliminating Japanese shipping in the South Pacific operating area. He also briefed them on the harassing missions that the Snoopers were flying, because, as he put it, "The Snoopers just ran the Japanese out of ships."

And Wagner and crew settled down for their first night on Los Negros.

Mission Briefing

June 11, 1944

Japanese surface vessels had almost been wiped out. The surface searches by the Snoopers had mostly resulted in wasted gasoline for more than a month.

General Matheny had no desire to waste 100-octane gasoline, but he needed a suitable assignment for the Snoopers. He couldn't use them as a part of the daily daylight bombing missions to Truk Atoll because the Snooper aircraft had radar in place of the belly gun turrets, and they would be instantly recognized by their charcoal-black color by the 100 or so Japanese fighters that swarmed up from Truk to meet the daylight bombers.

The general's solution was to assign the Snoopers to night harassing missions over Truk with the hopes that keeping the fighter pilots and antiaircraft gunners awake all night might make the enemy's aim less accurate.

It was a good solution. For a few weeks the Fifth and 307th Groups had made daily assaults on Truk with remarkably few casualties, in spite of being intercepted by ninety to one hundred Japanese Zeros on every mission. Fighter escort was out of the question because it was more than 750 miles from Los Negros Island, the operating base for the heavy bombers of the Thirteenth Air Force, to Truk.

1,400 Hours

First Sergeant Fisher ran down the row of tents that housed the officers of the Snooper squadron until he arrived at the tent of 2nd Lt. Jack Wagner.

"Lieutenant Wagner, sir, you and your crew are to report to the operations tent immediately for tonight's mission briefing." The response was more energetic and enthusiastic than usual for a Snooper aircraft commander. Lieutenant Wagner's crew, being new to the Snoopers, had been looking forward to their first real mission. All of the other Snooper crews had been through many night missions, and the members of the Wagner crew were anxious to become "real" Snoopers, so it wasn't surprising to see all ten members troop into the operations tent a few minutes later.

The briefing was short and sweet. Mostly the operations officer was concerned with two weather fronts between Mokerang and Truk. Since Wagner's crew was so new, the ops officer wasn't sure that they would rely on the radar to help them through the soft spots in the weather, so he dwelt on this subject at length. Finally he got down to the mission itself.

"You will bomb Dublontown from an altitude of 12,000 feet. If you have enough fuel, you will remain in the vicinity of Truk to harass and keep them awake, but don't get close enough to the islands to attract antiaircraft fire after you have gotten rid of your bombs. Are there any questions?"

The bombardier, 2nd. Charles Goerke, asked, "Which end of Dublontown do you want me to hit, Captain?"

Everybody, including the briefing officer, recognized this remark as Lt. Goerke's way of jesting, because Dublontown was just a dot on a very small island in the lagoon, so to general laughter, Captain Wiles announced that takeoff time would be 1930 hours, and the briefing was ended.

"All right, Crew, get some chow, get your gear together and be at the aircraft at 1750," Lieutenant Wagner called out as he went over to take a closer look at the weather map with Lieutenant Bonney, his navigator.

63

Nobody was really very hungry. First missions were always a nerve-wracking time for the crew members, even when they had trained together and flown halfway around the world together. Three hours remained until time to report to the aircraft; The copilot, 2nd Lt. Russ Pickering, went back to his tent and picked up the girlie magazine that he had been reading before the first sergeant called them; the navigator, Second Lieutenant Bonney, pulled out his octant and checked it over; the bombardier, Second Lieutenant Goerke, pulled out the situation map of Truk to review the locations of the islands and particularly the location of Dublontown. Lieutenant Goerke often jested about mission plans and mission conditions, but when it came to the job of bombing, he was all business. He realized that he would probably not have a very clear view of the target at night and, with the usual cloud cover that always hangs around the atolls, he knew that he would probably have to drop on the radar signals, but just in case he did get a visual sighting, he would be ready.

Flight engineer Hal Dotterer, radio operator Jerry Rokos, radar operator Merle Musey, assistant flight engineer Sgt. Clarence Wolfsberger, gunners Sgt. Charles Whitmore and Cpl. Len Davis all went to the mess hall and asked the cook to fix them some chow. They all had knots in their stomachs but none of them wanted to admit it.

Sergeant Wolfsberger was the oldest member of the crew and he was the only one who was married. With a first name like Clarence, he had acquired the nickname of "Pappy," and all of the crew looked to him for advice about their personal problems. Even the officers, who were all barely out of their teens, consulted Pappy. He was usually a tower of strength, but that day Pappy was as unsure of himself as any of them. As he sat there munching on the sandwich that the cook had fixed, his mind was on his bride back in Merced. Their second anniversary was approaching, and he knew that Suzy would be wondering where he was. All of the mail was censored, so he couldn't even write to her and let her know where he was; even if he could write, the mail took weeks to get back to the

States, according to the squadron members who had been over-seas for months and not just a few days, as he had. Pappy had heard the stories about schemes some of the guys had cooked up to let their wives know where they were without having the censors cut that information out of their letters. One of the sergeants had arranged with his wife that he would change his middle initial in his return address on each letter. All she had to do was put his letters in order of the dates and his middle initials would spell out his location. It worked fine until the censor opened one of her letters. She had written, "What does L-A-E mean?"

Staff Sergeant Rokos was poring over his radio procedures and checking frequency channels.

"Hey, Jerry," chided Sgt. Charles Whitmore. "That's a waste of time, we're going to be on [radio] silence for the whole mission. You'll have lots of time to check the frequencies on the way back."

"What about your radar, Merle?" retorted Jerry. "You're going to be blasting away with that honker all the way there and back."

"Aw, I checked with S-2 and he says that the Japs don't even know that there is an S-band, let alone have equipment to monitor it.

"Besides, if we have the weather that Captain Wiles said we would, Lieutenant Bonney is not only going to have to use the radar to find the soft spots, he'll need it to find Truk. There's a lot of ocean out there, and Truk is just a speck 750 miles from here, and no road map."

1745 Hours

The carryall pulled up at the mess hall and the Wagner crew climbed aboard. It was a short ride to the flight line, and they piled out and began loading their gear aboard.

What Does L-A-E Mean?

When General MacArthur arrived in Australia from Bataan in March 1942, he found scant forces there for the defensive action needed if the Japanese were to be stopped in their surge southward. Even so, he decided that the best way to protect Australia was to throw as much strength as he could into New Guinea, in order to hold the Japanese on the far side of the Owen Stanley Mountains and secure the vital Australian base at Port Moresby. The first Japanese try at taking Port Moresby resulted in the inconclusive Battle of the Coral Sea in May 1942.

Then on July 21, the Japanese landed at Buna, on the north coast, and proceeded to do what no one among the Allied strategists thought possible; they crossed the Owen Stanleys and drove on Port Moresby. By mid-September, at the time when the Allied campaign on Guadalcanal was looking very doubtful indeed, the Japanese were within thirty miles of Port Moresby. But General MacArthur rushed in troops and planes, and in the next ten months the Allies battled the Japanese back over the mountains, took Buna, and began the long drive up the northern coast of New Guinea that was to be one side of a giant pincers movement that would eventually isolate Rabaul, Japan's Gibraltar of the South Pacific.

General MacArthur had stopped the Japanese advance in New Guinea. The Japanese now tried to save their New Guinea forces by reinforcing the garrisons at Lae and Salamaua. On March 1, 1943, United States reconnaissance planes spotted a powerful imperial convoy carrying seven thousand troops and trying, under cover of bad weather, to make it from Rabaul through the Bismarck Sea to Lae on New Guinea's northeastern coast. Two days later, on March 3, in the major action of the three-day Battle of the Bismarck Sea, Maj. Gen. George C. Kenny's Fifth Air Force, operating from Papua, smashed the convoy and Japanese plans for holding New Guinea. By the time they had finished, they had sunk or damaged most of the ten warships and twelve transports in the formation, drowning all save a handful of the reinforcements. The Japanese had also lost one hundred and two aircraft in the engagement.

By midsummer of 1943, General MacArthur had four American divisions and six Australian divisions supported by Adm. William F. Halsey's South Pacific fleet. Admiral Nimitz had nine U.S. Army and Marine divisions in the central Pacific. With these relatively small forces, they stepped up the counterattack against strong Japanese dispositions in heavily fortified bases.

Within little more than a year, General MacArthur's effective and economical strategy had reached far up the southwest Pacific archipelagoes and severed 135,000 Japanese from all prospects of rescue.

Lae was one link in the chain that encircled the Imperial Japanese forces.

The O'Club

The officer's club on Los Negros Island was constructed by native labor. It was a large thatched building that was meant to house the leisure-time activities of 2,000 officers of the Thirteenth Air Force who were stationed on Los Negros and flew missions out of Momote Airfield and Mokerang Airfield. There was a large sign over the main entrance that read: "Lieutenant colonels under the age of twenty one years must be accompanied by their parents when patronizing this club."

Promotions came fast in the Thirteenth—to those who survived. The attrition rate among the fighter pilots and the medium bomber pilots was frighteningly high. Colonel Wright had warned the crews of the 868th that the losses might run as high as 50 percent, but the Snooper crews knew that they were special crews on a special mission. The successes that they had experienced in the first year of operations gave them the heady feeling that they were virtually invincible. The O'Club was a place to relax and exchange hairy tales and talk small talk and forget for a few minutes the fact that there would be another mission in a few days or a few hours.

One of the favorite pastimes was to swap stories about the rest leaves in Sydney or Auckland. Captain Anger had a favorite that he told over and over. He never lost a chance to unload it on a new crew and, since Lieutenant Wagner's crew was the newest crew around, he just "happened" to sit with them one night after they arrived at the squadron.

This was Captain Anger's rest leave story:

68

"We were still operating out of Munda and our rest leave area was Auckland. I was the ranking flying officer in the group that was given two weeks leave and that meant that I had to fly the C-47 from Munda to Noumea, New Caledonia, and after an overnight rest, fly on to Auckland. The weather was rotten enough from Munda to Noumea, but from Noumea to Auckland, it was a mess. I think the airplane was upside down more than it was right side up and everybody was airsick. We didn't have a Snooper radar in the C-47 so the best I could do was try to pick out the light spots visually and fly through. We finally broke out of the weather about 100 miles northwest of Auckland and landed with clear skies and bright sunshine. I taxied the C-47 up to the ramp, shut down the engines, locked the brakes and gave a big sigh of relief. I was too tired to even get up and get out of the airplane.

"Lieutenant Crowe had been in Auckland for about a month. He had been sent to the station hospital for a hemorrhoidectomy, Auckland having the only station hospital in the South Pacific area. After the first few days in the hospital he was ambulatory, and being the wild and wooly big-time operator that he was, he had really made a lot of contacts among the citizenry.

"Lieutenant Crowe and I were great friends at Munda, and he knew when he went to Auckland that I was due for a rest leave soon, so he was looking for my name on the flight status board at the airport. When he saw my name on the arrival board, he was there to meet the airplane. The passengers had barely gotten off when Lieutenant Crowe came racing up through the passenger compartment and buttonholed me in the cabin.

" 'Steve,' he said. 'Boy am I glad to see you. We have a great party planned for tonight and you're invited.'

" 'Chuck, I am wiped out from dancing on these rudder pedals all day. I'm in no shape for partying tonight.'

" 'Aw, come on, Steve. I've set you up with a date and she is really going to be disappointed if you don't show.'

" 'Look, Chuck, I'm hungry as a bear and I'm going to eat

before I tap out. How about if I take her out to dinner, as long as she understands that I won't last very long after that?'

" 'Let's give her a call on the phone.' "

"Her name was Angie. We called her on the phone and she was very understanding. She agreed to the dinner and a short evening and I agreed to pick her up as soon as I had changed clothes and gotten cleaned up. I went to the Kia-Ora where I had a room and then caught a taxi to Angie's address. When she came to the door she was in a dressing gown and obviously not ready to leave for dinner. I paid off the taxi driver and told him I would call him. Angie fixed a couple of drinks and started to chitchat. After about five minutes, I said, 'Look, Angie, I'm not going to last very long. Why don't you get dressed so we can go out to dinner?"

"Angie looked me straight in the eye and replied, 'Oh, let's have a bit of a go at it first, shall we?"

"I didn't miss dinner at all."

Drinks at the club were fifteen cents. Even in those days, when a Second Lieutenant's base pay was $115 (per month), it was still possible to get smashed every night if you had that inclination. There were significant numbers of officers who had that inclination. Almost every night a group of (more than social) drinkers would end up at one end of the bar singing songs and telling risque stories until either the bar closed or the OD came in and closed the bar because the racket was disturbing local residents. One of the favorite songs was:

I've got sixpence; jolly, jolly sixpence. I've got sixpence to last
    me all my life. I've got tuppence to spend and tuppence to
    lend, And tuppence to send home to my wife (poor wife).
Rolling home, rolling home, by the light of the silvery
    moo-oo-oo-oon.
      Happy is the day, when the airman gets his pay, as
    we go rolling, rolling home.
I've got tuppence; jolly, jolly tuppence. I've got tuppence to last
    me all my life. I've got tuppence to spend and no-pence

to lend, And no-pence to send home to my wife, (poor wife).

This song had to be repeated at least ten times until the whole crew began to sober up because they couldn't drink and sing at the same time.

When "Sixpence" began to lose steam, the dirty limericks would start, usually with the hermit named Dave and proceeding through worse and worse ones until they reached the young girl from the Azores, who provided not only the climax of the singing, but also the evening.

About the only sporting activity in the club was a Ping-Pong table. A new Ping-Pong champion had to be selected every night. If one man fought his way to the top for several nights in a row, it was a rule that everyone interested in the game would buy him a drink.

At fifteen cents a throw it really didn't put much of a burden on anyone, and by the time he had downed all the offered drinks, he probably was seeing more than one ball and didn't know which one to return. So the championship would rotate through the whole Thirteenth Air Force.

Card games were big in the club. Red Dog games would continue for days. If the bar closed, the pot would be saved for the next night and the names of the players would be carefully recorded so their interests would be protected.

There was a continual gin rummy contest going, usually over in one corner of the club with a waiting line of replacements for the loser. The stakes were a penny a point, ten cents a book and a dollar a game; everything double for skunks. It was pretty hard to lose more than a couple of dollars in an evening.

The Fifty-eighth Evacuation Hospital was located on Los Negros and there were several female nurses on the staff. They had very little time off because of the continual flow of wounded through the hospital, but when they did have time off they would visit the club. It was a great morale builder to have ladies from the United States make their presence visible in an area where there were literally zero women in the day-to-day working/living areas.

The Snooper officers who patronized the club had a problem

with the officers of the Fifth, Forty-third, and 307th groups. The Snooper aircraft were equipped with equipment that had security classification of "SECRET," and none of the other officers were cleared for access to the information as to what the gear was or how it worked. They were all curious about those coal-black B-24s that were parked in a remote area of Mokerang with armed guards around them, but the dedication that Colonel Wright had instilled saved the Snoopers from breaking security.

Tokyo Rose

The Joker flew like an angel. Her engines were practically brand new and they had never been overtaxed. Taking off from Mokerang with a gross weight of 69,000 pounds was certainly taxing, but Lieutenant Wagner eased back on the elevator trim tab at 115 knots and danced on the rudder pedals as *The Joker,* mildly complaining and a little unsteady, came off the runway and inched upward.

"Wheels up," said Lieutenant Wagner to copilot Pickering.

"Roger. Wheels up." Thirty seconds passed while *The Joker* clawed at the air for enough altitude to start raising the flaps.

"Ten degrees, flaps," said Lieutenant Wagner.

"Roger. Ten degrees," replied Lieutenant Pickering.

The engines were still at full military power, but with the wheels up and the flaps coming up, the rate of climb was creeping up to 500 feet per minute. At 2,500 feet altitude, Lieutenant Wagner called for flaps up and eased the nose down so he could fly level and reduce the engine power to 2,250 RPM and thirty five inches of mercury. At that power setting he could fly level at 140 knots. He knew that he would have to fly at that speed for at least two hours until the fuel had been reduced so he could put the aircraft into optimum cruise configuration. At 2,250 RPM and thirty five inches manifold pressure, each of the Pratt-Whitney 2280 engines would use seventy five gallons of fuel per hour, and that would get rid of a ton of gross weight per hour, but to complete the mission the transition had to be accomplished as early as possible or they would run out of fuel on the way home.

"Skipper, I've got Tokyo Rose on the BC-348," Staff Sergeant Rokos announced on the intercom. "If you want me to, I'll patch it into the com line." Such a patch was strictly against standard operating procedures, but many of the crews on night harassing missions listened to short-wave broadcasts as a defense against the sheer boredom of fifteen hours on a black-dark night in a noisy, vibrating machine. Staff Sergeant Rokos had made the unauthorized patch cord in the radar repair shop, which was outfitted with more tools and equipment than most of the communication shops.

"Okay," replied Lieutenant Wagner, "but keep it low enough so we can talk over the top of it."

"Roger, sir," replied Staff Sergeant Rokos.

The strains of Glen Miller's "String of Pearls" drifted out of the headsets, kind of tinny, but recognizable. As "String of Pearls" came to an end, an announcer came on abruptly.

"This musical interlude had been brought to you through the courtesy of Tooth-o tooth paste. Tooth-o tooth paste will keep your teeth pearly white; it works while you sleep." And then came the velvety voice of Tokyo Rose.

"We know that you GIs miss your soap operas while you are fighting and dying in the South Pacific jungles, so as a part of our public service, we will present the next episode of *One GI's Family*."

Organ music rose and then softened. A female voice spoke.

"Oh, John, I don't want to go *up-stairs* with you tonight. I'm feeling so guilty cheating on George while he is off in the South Pacific fighting this terrible war. Please go."

"But Mary," replied a male voice, "I have a new French tickler that is guaranteed to give you the thrill of a lifetime."

"No, John, I've made up my mind. I will be true to George until he comes home.'

"All right, if that's the way you feel, I won't be seeing you anymore."

Footsteps, and a door closed.

"Oh, goody," said Mary, "Now I can call my new boyfriend, Paul. He is so much younger and livelier than that creep, John."

Organ music came up and faded away. The voice of Tokyo Rose returned.

"That was quite a party we had over Truk Island yesterday. You boys in the Fifth and 307th groups sure took a beating from our imperial fighter pilots. They reported seven B-24s disabled and probably had to land in the water before they reached home base. It's too bad those poor boys had to give their lives for a fruitless operation. None of the bombs fell on the islands, most fell in the lagoon. The poor fish took the brunt of your attack.

"And now I would like to send a message to the boys in the 868th Squadron. I know that you think that black paint will save you from our fighters at night, but I want to assure you that you cannot escape the detectors that we have protecting our installations. If you try any more of that night harassing, you can expect to be punished."

Tokyo Rose played several of the most popular tunes that were on the air in the United States and continued with her diatribes against the British and American warmongers.

Finally, Lieutenant Wagner called out over the intercom, "Sergeant Rokos, it's time that we get into combat configuration. Kill Tokyo Rose and let's check out equipment."

"Roger, Skipper. All radio gear stowed."

Random Thoughts on a Dark Night

After Tokyo Rose was turned off, there was very little talk on the intercom. Lieutenant Jack Wagner was resting with his seat down, letting the Honeywell autopilot fly *The Joker*. The weather at 12,000 feet was generally clear and smooth. He knew that Lieutenant Tom Bonney would keep a DR log, and if they strayed too far off course for Truk, Tom would give him a new heading; besides, everyone in the aircraft knew that the radar would pick up Truk from a distance of 100 miles and there would be no way they could be off course that far.

Lieutenant Russ Pickering was checking the instrument panel in a continuous cycle. Jack looked up now and then to see Russ's index finger point from manifold pressure to RPM to altimeter to airspeed to voltage on the power bus and then to an array of warning lights; when everything was normal, he started over with the manifold pressure.

At 12,000 feet altitude, it was cold. They had left Mokerang six hours before and the temperature had been 85 degrees and humid enough to be muggy; now the temperature in the B-24 was 10 degrees and there were enough holes around the gun turrets and windows that it would have been sheer misery without the flight jackets, flight pants and boots, and flight helmets. They were uncomfortable enough for the pilot, copilot, navigator, bombardier, and gunners in the power turrets, but for the gunners in the waist positions they were so clumsy that just moving around was exhausting, especially at 12,000 feet altitude where the air was thin. By rights, they should have all been on oxygen at that altitude, but wearing the oxygen masks for several hours was worse than being dragged down by borderline anoxia, so nobody was wearing a mask. They would put them on when they were about an hour out from Truk.

Lieutenant Wagner was thinking about the Red Dog game they had been playing at Carney. The game had actually been going on for days, and they just sat in for a day or two, off and on as they felt like it. It was a friendly game with each player getting four cards (instead of three, like that cutthroat game that had been going on at Buttons when they went through), so the pot never really got too big, but at one point it had accumulated to $120 when he had received a hand of three aces and the queen in the fourth suit. He didn't have $120 in his wallet, so he asked Lieutenant Pickering and Lieutenant Goerke if they would back him if he lost. They both said they would, so he called the pot. His match card came up a seven in the queen's suit. Jack smiled, somewhere between daydreaming and falling asleep, and then he really dozed for several minutes.

Lieutenant Pickering didn't have much time to do anything except step from one gauge to the next. He knew that Jack was resting and even with "George" flying *The Joker,* it was necessary to keep an eye on the gauges just in case something should malfunction. Russ was already looking ahead to their first rest leave in Sydney, Australia. He had heard tales of the friendly people, especially the girls, and to say that they intrigued him would be putting it mildly. He was a product of midwestern United States society of the 1930s. He didn't really have a girlfriend while he was in high school or his first two years of college, and his social life revolved around a few school buddies who were all interested in cars. Russ had salvaged an old Essex Terraplane and gotten it running so that he could drive to high school instead of taking the bus, which (owning a car) was a status symbol among his buddies. He had had a dream of salvaging an airplane and getting it running, but the cost was far beyond his meager earnings from doing part-time jobs in the small town where he had lived. When the draft came along,

Russ had applied for pilot training and was granted a one-year deferment to finish his first two years of college so he could enter cadet training at Randolph.

He was thinking about the days he spent at Randolph and the hazings he took from the flight instructors when Staff Sergeant Musey spoke on the intercom.

"Radar to pilot: we're approaching a cumulus cloud that is at this altitude. Unless we turn away, we'll go right through the middle of it and it looks pretty rough on the radar."

"Copilot to radar: Roger, I'll check with the navigator."

"Copilot to navigator: What do you want to do about the storm? Should we go through or do you want to go around it?"

"I've got it on my scope, Russ. Turn right ten degrees and hold it for twenty minutes. Truk should show up on the radar about that time and we can turn straight toward it."

"Roger."

The air raid siren at Truk sounded just after midnight. The audio detectors had heard *The Joker* as it rounded the cumulus cloud and turned toward the atoll. Warrant Officer Nakagawa was roughly jerked out of a deep sleep by the rising and falling siren. He shook himself and ran to his Gekko. He had been working all day to repair damage that was done during the day raid by falling debris, and he had slept so hard that he was still a little groggy when he got to the revetments area and began climbing into his flight suit. The grogginess soon left him when he climbed into the Gekko and began going down the checklist prior to engine start. The problems with the Gekko were not engine problems; he was most concerned about dents that had been made on the wing and control surfaces. Debris from bomb craters and shrapnel from antiaircraft guns that had been firing at the day bombers during the daylight bombing had landed on his Gekko and caused the dents. Because of the severe shortage of aviation gasoline on the island, Nakagawa could not get permission to make a test flight to confirm that the repairs had remedied the damage, so he would just have to take a chance that the Gekko would fly properly.

The night was black-dark. The moon would not be up for another hour or more and the islands were so blacked out that Nakagawa had little visibility of anything outside the cabin of his Gekko. The engines started at the first try and his wing walkers with their tiny little lights that looked like fireflies signalled him to tap off the brakes; they would guide him to the end of the runway.

The runway was in even worse shape than the last time he had taken off, but Warrant Officer Nakagawa bumped over craters and finally got the Gekko into the air. This time the Gekko did not fly as smoothly as usual. The ailerons were far out of alignment, so he had to hold the wheel far over to the left to keep the Gekko level. Nakagawa rolled in trim to compensate and at the same time kept track of the rate of climb. The Gekko's engines were operating perfectly, so his rate of climb was more than 1,500 feet per minute in spite of the full load of fuel and the 2,000 rounds of twenty-mm cannon shells that he was carrying.

Warrant Officer Nakagawa had flown this night-fighter mission so many times that it was almost by rote that he climbed to 10,000 feet altitude and began a series of figure eight patterns across the meridian south from the central islands of Truk Atoll. He knew that he had a few minutes before the harassing bomber would be close enough to Truk to be illuminated by the searchlight, and until the searchlight came on, all he could do would be to time out his figure eight patterns and keep checking his engine instruments to be sure the Gekko was operating properly. His thoughts drifted back to the early days of the war when he flew successful sorties against the Americans in the Philippines and in the sweep of the Japanese navy down the Celebes and finally on to New Guinea. He had been flying Mark II Zeroes in those days and they were so superior to the P-400s flown by the Americans and British colonials that Warrant Officer Nakagawa thought the war would be over in less than six months, but now he realized that the Japanese high command had not accounted for the adaptability of the Americans, because here they were, almost three years later, fighting a different kind of war, a defensive war that seemed to have no end. He thought of his home in Yokohama that he had not seen for more than three years and he worried about the welfare of his family, who were subsisting on less than adequate food and who had suffered through a bitter cold winter with inadequate fuel.

Warrant Officer Nakagawa suddenly shook himself out of these depressing reveries and took a good look around the area. The searchlight was not on yet, so he made another check of the engines to be sure that they were performing properly. Now that he had trimmed the Gekko, it was flying smoothly, and he made a mental note that he should inspect the ailerons to see why it was necessary to trim so far to the left.

Suddenly, the searchlight came on and the harassing aircraft was illuminated. Warrant Officer Nakagawa turned his Gekko toward the illuminated B-24 and waited for the antiaircraft fire to commence and then end.

As *The Joker* passed the big cumulus cloud, Staff-Sergeant Musey called out on the intercom, "Land target five degrees left at 105 nautical miles."

"Roger, Radar. This is the pilot. All crew members be on alert. We will be over the target in forty minutes and we may be intercepted on the approach. All stations report."

"Bombardier, ready."

"Nose Turret, ready."

"Top Turret ready."

"Tail Guns, ready."

"Radar, ready."

There was pause for several minutes, and then:

"Radar, this is the bombardier, give me a thirty-degree sector scan centered on twelve o'clock."

"Radar, Roger. Sector scan thirty degrees at twelve o'clock."

"Bombardier to pilot: Jack, I can't see anything visually so I'm going to set up the computer to drop on the radar signal from Eton Island. Coming in from the south, if I initiate on the near edge of the island, the bombs should fall right across Dublontown."

"Pilot to bombardier: Roger, Chuck. Tell me when you are driving the API."

The API was an instrument on the pilot's instrument panel that took data from the Norden bombsight or from the radar computer and showed the pilot which direction to turn the plane to point it directly toward the target. No—that isn't quite right. It told the pilot which direction to turn the airplane so that the line of flight of the bombs would be directly over the target. In some situations, the output of the API would be connected directly into the Honeywell autopilot so that the bombardier was really in direct control of the airplane while on the bombing run. Lieutenant Wagner had decided not to put the airplane in that configuration for this mission because, in case they were attacked by the night fighter, he might need to take evasive action quickly and would not want the delay of disconnecting the API from the autopilot.

"Pilot to crew: I'm going on manual flight control, so I can take evasive action if I have to. All stations be alert for interceptors."

"Roger," came back over the intercom from five different sources.

Ten miles from the atoll, the searchlight caught them and hung on like a leech. Thirty seconds after the searchlight came on, the antiaircraft shells began bursting. *The Joker* shuddered occasionally when a shell burst close by, but none of them made any impact on the aircraft and everyone on board just gritted their teeth and kept a careful watch for interceptors.

Warrant Officer Nakagawa saw the first antiaircraft shells burst near the B-24 and he checked the time on his panel clock. One minute later he opened the throttles and rapidly closed the distance between his Gekko and the enemy aircraft. Due to the damaged aileron control, the Gekko tended to roll to the left with the increased power. Nakagawa trimmed to compensate; in the process he overshot the approach so that he was too far forward, and when he reduced power the Gekko rolled to the right. It took him longer than he would have liked to get lined up on the aircraft, and when he finally fired his cannon he saw that he was hitting the right wing tip; he quickly rolled the Gekko to the left and watched as a series of bursts walked down the right wing, across the fuselage, and out to the left wing tip.

Because of his experience with the break-up of Lieutenant Arthur's airplane and the dangerous debris that showered down from it, Warrant Officer Nakagawa immediately rolled GEKKO over on its back and did a split-S to get out of the way. He also reported the enemy destroyed on his radio and headed back to base.

When the antiaircraft shells stopped exploding, everyone on *The Joker* knew that an interceptor was in the area. Because they were on the bomb run, Lieutenant Wagner had to hold the airplane steady, and because of Warrant Officer Nakagawa overshooting his intended approach, he came up under *The Joker* in an absolute blind spot to everyone on board. Lieutenant Wagner saw the first burst of a twenty millimeter shell on the right wing tip, and he leaned over, frozen, as the shells walked across the right wing and then out across the left wing. Wagner tried to roll the aircraft to the left but there was no response to the aileron control. He pushed the control column forward to dive away and again there was no response. He kicked right rudder and *The Joker* yawed to the right. His instruments told him that the aircraft was still flying, but he was losing altitude rapidly and the sounds around him were pandemonium. The holes in the bottom of the wings roared at him, two engines were out and windmilling, aviation gasoline was pouring into the bomb bay so fast that there was no oxygen for it to burn. Luckily he and all the crew were on oxygen, so the fumes didn't incapacitate them.

Miracle of miracles—the electrical system was still working. Wagner's instruments told him that the number one engine and the number three engine were both dead and windmilling. He asked Lieutenant Pickering to feather them, but Russ replied that the feathering switches didn't work. He tried to level out their descent with the elevator trim tab, but there was no response. A quick check of the Honeywell autopilot showed that it was still working. It had no control over the ailerons, but it did control the elevator and the rudders.

"Pilot calling," he called into the intercom. "Is anybody on here?" Immediately a chorus of "Roger's" came back.

"Pilot to crew: Report!"

"Bombardier. Roger."

"Nose Turret. Roger."

"Top Turret. Roger."

"Tail Turret. Roger."

"Waist Gunner. Roger."

"Radar. Roger."

"Okay, crew, the navigator and radio operator are up here with me on the flight deck. We're still flying and everybody seems to be alive. I'm going to have to make a water landing, so everybody get braced for impact."

Lieutenant Wagner tried the engine controls and found that in addition to engines one and three being out and windmilling, number two was locked at 75 percent power and he couldn't move it because the control cable was cut. *The Joker* had been in a wide sweeping left turn from the time of the attack and the altimeter was winding down very determinedly. As the heading changed from north to west and then to south, Lieutenant Wagner realized that the moon had just come up and by careful control of the autopilot, he would be able to time their impact with the water to their heading into the moon. This would allow the waist gunner to look "up-moon" and give warning when they were about to impact.

"Pilot to navigator: Tom, do you have any idea where we are?"

"Sure, Jack. We're over the west edge of the Truk reef and it looks to me like you are going to land in the lagoon."

"In the *lagoon!* We'll be captured for sure, but there isn't anything I can do about it. This beat-up crate isn't going to fly much farther!"

Down and Out in Truk Lagoon

"Pilot to nose turret and bombardier: Get out of the nose and get into the waist. Navigator and RO, get out of the flight deck and into the waist."

"Roger, Nose Turret."

"Roger, Bombardier."

"Roger, Navigator."

"Roger, Radio."

"Pilot to navigator: Look toward the moon and tell me when we are getting close to the water. The radar altimeter isn't working."

"Roger, Navigator."

"Everybody in the waist, brace yourselves."

The antenna for the radar altimeter protruded from the bottom of the aircraft very near the center of gravity. One of the twenty-mm shells had wiped it off, and the radar altimeter, which could have given Lieutenant Wagner information on the height above the water, was useless. The pressure altitude was not accurate enough to be used for a water landing because it had been set to the barometric pressure at Mokerang before they departed. At sea level, one-tenth of an inch of mercury change in the barometric pressure would result in 1,000 feet of altitude error on the altimeter. With *The Joker* descending at about 1,000 feet per minute, Lieutenant Wagner didn't have much time to contemplate his alternatives. He chose to take a warning of low altitude from the waist and try for a nose high stall as near the water as possible.

It had only been ten minutes since they were shot up; the gasoline had stopped pouring into the bomb bay, but it was still more than a trickle. Staff Sergeant Dotterer had transferred fuel from the bomb-bay tanks to the wing tanks about an hour before they arrived over Truk. The bombardier, Lieutenant Goerke, had gotten rid of the bombs and closed the bomb-bay doors just before they were shot up, and the gas that had poured out of the wing tanks had quickly leaked out of the sides and ends of the bomb-bay doors. By the time *The Joker* had descended to sea level, there was very little residual weight in the aircraft. The two operating engines were running on the fuel that was sloshing around in the bottom of the wing fuel tanks.

"Navigator to pilot: Fifty feet."

"Roger, Tom. See if you can call out ten feet." With the rate of descent at 1,000 feet per minute, there were only three seconds between fifty feet and impact. Lieutenant Wagner put in a "nose up" command to the autopilot and *The Joker* began to level off. The airspeed dropped off dramatically because of the gaping holes in the wings from the cannon bursts, so even before the flight path had quite reached level, *The Joker* hit the water and bounced once, twice, three times, and came to a shuddering stop. The intercom died immediately, but there was no need to tell the crew what to do; they had been through the ditching procedure so many times that it was like clockwork.

Sergeant Whitmore was a nonswimmer so Staff Sergeant Musey pulled the cords on his "Mae West" and kicked him out through the waist window. Staff Sergeant Dotterer was stunned by the impact. He woke up underwater with his Mae West inflated and floated out of a hole in the fuselage between the bomb bay and the waist. They were all in their two rubber rafts, all emergency equipment was out and stowed and the emergency foods were on board. The procedure took less than three minutes. Then they sat there beside *The Joker,* which floated for more than ten minutes after the water impact. Lieutenant Wagner stood on the left wing and called the roll. Lieutenant Pickering and Sergeant Wolfsberger were missing and could not be found.

A Not-so-Sleepy Lagoon

The Joker sank very majestically. Hardly a ripple marked her descent to the bottom of the lagoon. A few bubbles broke on the surface for a few minutes and that was it.

"Tom, do you have any idea what part of the lagoon we're in?" asked Lieutenant Wagener.

"I think we are near the south reef, Jack, but I would hate to make an estimate of how far we are from it."

"All right, Crew, we are down near one of the primary Japanese naval bases in the world. Let's be quiet and see if they can overlook us. It's too near sunrise for us to try to paddle out through the reef because there are machine gun emplacements on that reef to repel invasions, so let's be quiet and see if we can be ignored today. Tonight we can try to get out through the reef and maybe find the submarine that was supposed to be ready to pick us up if we had to land in the water. Everybody be quiet and don't even talk loud." Lieutenant Wagner was talking in a stage whisper.

The first hour was devoted to stowing supplies and survival gear. Anything that looked the least bit sharp went overboard; shoes, belts, insignia: anything that might puncture a raft. Everyone looked around to see if they could see anything that looked like an island or a gun emplacement or anything that looked like a Japanese installation. There was nothing that they could see in the light of the gibbous moon. Lieutenant Bonney had kept his maps with him, wrapped in a waterproof cover and tucked inside his flight jacket. He didn't dare show a light to try to pinpoint their location, and the moonlight was too dim to allow the map to be read, so he put it away to await the sunrise. All of the crew were wearing their flight jackets, pants, and boots. Very soon after they got into the rubber life rafts, they began shedding the suits and stashing them in the bottom of the rafts. As the eastern sky turned pink and then red, Lieutenant Wagner called for the blue cloth that would make them more inconspicuous to any aircraft flying overhead. When they examined the cloth, they found it was only big enough for one raft. Up until that time, the rafts had been lashed together end to end, but with the realization that they only had one camouflage cloth, the men pulled the rafts together so they were side by side. They hoped that that way they would be able to pass the blue cloth around and keep it between them and any aircraft that passed overhead.

The Truk lagoon contains more than 823 square miles of water and land area. The total land area of the fifty small islands and reef areas that are above mean sea level is less than forty square miles, so it was understandable that somewhere in the lagoon a couple of small rubber rafts could be overlooked. They would be hard to find even if the Japanese were looking for them. The Japanese had no reason to look for them after Warrant Officer Nakagawa gave his report of his attack. He was convinced and he convinced his superiors that the aircraft was totally destroyed by the fifty or more twenty-mm cannon shells that he saw explode on the wings and fuselage.

Sunrise came with scattered cumulus clouds over the lagoon. Everyone in the crew kept a sharp eye out for anything that would give them a clue as to where they were. They were sure now that they were in the lagoon because the water was too calm to be broad ocean area. The question was, where in the 800 square miles of the lagoon were they? Their first clue came when a reconnaissance plane took off from the runway at Eton Island. Lieutenant Bonney looked at the compass and estimated that they were south-southeast of the runway. Judging by the appearance of the aircraft, he thought they were at least ten miles from Eton island. That would put them about five miles from the south reef. His compass also verified that the northeast trade wind was blowing them toward the south and west. He recommended to Lieutenant Wagner that they let the wind blow them toward the south reef until they could see gun emplacements or other evidence that they were getting near the reef and then they should put out a sea anchor to hold position until nightfall. An occasional shower would drop from the little cumulus clouds that drifted overhead. All the crew members who could, helped hold up cloths and jackets and anything that would catch the fresh water and collect it in the rubber buckets that were part of the emergency equipment.

At 10:00 A.M., a Japanese Zero fighter flew almost directly over the rafts. It was obviously on a reconnaissance mission, and the crew passed the blue cloth around to try to keep out of his sight. There was so much debris around that they were astonished that he didn't see them. Wheels, bomb-bay tanks and anything that floated out of the aircraft was near the rafts, although, since the rafts floated higher in the water than the debris, the debris was generally upwind.

Sergeant Musey had broken his right wrist getting out of *The Joker* and Lieutenant Wagner had dislocated his shoulder when *The Joker* hit the water. All the rest of the crew who survived were unhurt except for some minor scrapes and bruises.

Exactly at noon, Zekes and Hamps began taking off in both directions from the runway on Eton Island. Those that took off into the wind to the northeast made a lefthand pattern and were above 8,000 feet altitude when they passed near the rafts, but some of the fighters were taking off downwind (the trade wind was only blowing about seven knots) and when they made their lefthand pattern they would pass overhead at less than 5,000 feet. The crew was busy passing the blue cloth around, trying to keep it between the rafts and the fighters that went overhead. This meant that at least eighty fighters were going to attack the day-bombing B-24s that had been detected by the audio sensors.

Soon—very soon—the drone of the B-24s was audible without sensors. At first, when they were out south of the atoll, they were hidden in the rows of scattered cumulus that hung around the edges of the lagoon. Then they broke out into the clear sky between clouds. Everybody in the raft had the urge to stand up and cheer, but they remembered Lieutenant Wagner's warning about being quiet.

The downed air crew had a grandstand seat at one of the greatest aerial dogfights in the WWII's Pacific arena. They watched forty B-24s coming in unescorted to a major Japanese stronghold that was being fanatically defended by eighty of the best fighter planes and pilots that the Japanese could field. The bombers came in at 17,000 feet altitude, which was almost the optimum altitude for the fighters. The bombers dropped their bombs: the fighters made numerous passes at the formation. In twenty minutes it was all over. There was no way to count the fighters returning to Eton because they were landing in the northeast, too far away.

After the aerial combat was over, everything seemed to get very quiet. Everyone in the crew was silent, each one veiled in his own thoughts about the crew members who must have been wounded or killed in the dogfight and how any one of them might have had the same fate the night before had it not been for a miraculous lucky break.

It seemed like a long time before the sun went down, and even with the trade wind blowing them toward the reef, there was no sign of any Japanese installations in the direction of their drifting. Shortly after sunset, the sound of breakers was heard. The paddles were unshipped and the rafts were paddled toward the sound of the surf. It was so dark that the only thing that could be seen was the phosphorescence of the waves breaking outside the reef. As they approached the reef, they realized that the tide was going out and a current was rushing out of a gap in the reef. They were very quiet now, because they had no idea of how near they might be to a machine gun emplacement. The current carried them swiftly through the reef and out into the open ocean. Immediately, waves began to pitch and toss the rafts.

Lieutenant Wagner, Lieutenant Bonney, Staff Sergeant

Dotterer, and Staff Sergeant Rokos were in one raft, and Lieutenant Goerke, Staff Sergeant Musey, Sergeant Whitmore, and Corporal Davis were in the other raft. During the first night in the open ocean, Lieutenant Goerke noticed that their raft was beginning to get a little limp.

"Jack, I think we have a slow leak in this raft."

"Take turns keeping it pumped up until daylight, Chuck. We can patch it then."

A rotating shift was set up to allow the raft to be kept inflated. It was obviously a slow leak but it required that someone keep awake. When the raft became soft, it would be reinflated with the hand pump.

The trade wind was still blowing them to the southwest but quite slowly. Lieutenant Bonney estimated that they were traveling about five miles per hour, fast enough to get them well out of sight of Truk by the next sunrise.

After an hour or two in the open ocean, everyone agreed that they were well out of earshot of any installations on the reef that might be occupied by Japanese soldiers or marines, so the stage whispers gave way to more open conversation.

"Jack, what happened to Russ and Sergeant Wolfsberger?" asked Lieutenant Bonney.

"Well, Tom, you know we hit the water pretty hard after that third skip, and the top turret came down into the flight deck. Sergeant Wolfsberger was standing between me and Russ and he took the full impact. I'm sure he was crushed. I had no idea *The Joker* would float as long as she did, so I went out through the hatch in a big hurry and I thought Russ was right behind me, but he must have been injured—he probably couldn't make it out. I really didn't know he was missing until I took the roll. By that time the flight deck was underwater and I couldn't go back."

"How's your shoulder?"

"I still can't use my right arm. I think I took a hit from the turret, too."

"Tom, do you think we should hoist a sail and try to make more speed away from this atoll?" asked Lieutenant Wagner.

"No, Jack, we are doing all right. We should be at least fifty miles from the atoll by sunrise and we will have a better chance of doing a good job of getting up a working sail than we would in the dark."

"Chuck," Lieutenant Wagner called out to Lieutenant Goerke in the other raft, "who have you got on pump duty?"

"Sergeant Whitmore, Jack. He is going to take it until he gets tired and then Staff Sergeant Musey will take it. We are trying to keep from taking too much water from the waves."

"Okay, Chuck. The rest of you try to get some sleep. We are going to have to patch your raft as soon as it is daylight."

When the moon came up, Staff Sergeant Musey was keeping the raft inflated but he knew it was an hour past midnight, and the sun would be coming up at 5:00 A.M.

Overdue and . . .

June 12, 1944

The Joker and Wagner's crew had been due back at Mokerang at 0600 hours. By 0630 the operations duty officer reported them overdue to Fifth Group Headquarters and to Thirteenth Bomber Command Headquarters. Major Barlow was up and in the operations tent with Capt. Ed Ackley, the intelligence officer. A call was placed to the naval liaison officer at Momote asking if the rescue submarine stationed in the vicinity of Truk had either reported seeing a B-24 going down or if, by chance, they had picked up the crew of *The Joker*.

It was after noon before there was an answer from the liaison officer: negative on both counts. The submarine had not seen anything that would verify that *The Joker* had gone down in the vicinity of Truk and they had not receive any survivors.

By noon, everyone in the Snooper camp was aware that Lieutenant Wagner and crew were not only overdue, but that they would have been out of fuel by 0800. This news had a sobering effect on the whole camp. Even though Wagner and crew had not been at the squadron long enough to generate close friends, an aura of gloom settled over the men who were flying the same kinds of missions as the ones who were lost.

After noon, Lieutenant Hesselden, the squadron adjutant, began the unwelcome task of gathering up the possessions of the crew and boxing them up to be sent home. Major Barlow began writing personal letters to the next of kin of each man on Wagner's crew. Chaplain Reichert helped with the letter writing, but with or without help, the duty of saying something personal that would be meaningful to the surviving relatives really fell on the major. That's a tough job when you know the men well and have developed a respect for them that has grown out of successful missions performed together, but in this case, a brand-new crew, men who had just joined the squadron a few days before and had gone on their first mission, had apparently been swallowed up by the Pacific Ocean. What could he say?

Dear Parent (or spouse, or sibling), As I write this letter, I know that you have been notified by telegram that your son (or spouse, or sibling) is missing and is presumed to be either dead or a prisoner of the Japanese. I can tell you very little more than that about the events that led to him being missing. I can tell you that he was doing a job that he wanted to do. It was an important job that will make a difference in the conflict between the United States of America and the Empire of Japan and, we all hope, speed the day when the forces of Japan will be vanquished.

The 868th bombardment Squadron is a very special squadron. Your son (or spouse, or sibling) was an exceptional airman and because of his outstanding ability was selected to fly with us. The fact that he was lost on the first mission that he flew with us does not detract in any way from the importance and effectiveness of his mission.

I can only add that I am also transmitting the heartfelt condolences of every man in the 868th with this letter.

Yours, most sincerely,
James Barlow, Comdr.

"Padre, how much good do these letters do to blunt the pain of losing a son or a husband or a brother these people have raised or grown up with or loved for years? Here I am trying to soften the blow, and I only knew these kids for a few days."

"Major, it's never easy to write letters like this even when you've lived with the lost airmen for a long time. Lieutenant Wagner and crew is a special case for you because they went down on their first mission. I can say very little more than that, 'It was God's will.' "

"That's trite, Padre. What am I going to say to the other crews who have to fly harassing missions over Truk? Am I supposed to say 'Via con Dios, guys, but watch out for Jap fighters'?"

"No, Major, the best thing to do is get the best information possible about the dangers they have to face and work out a solution. Our airmen are the most adaptable, professional fliers in the world. We neutralized the Japanese garrison at Rabaul, and we will neutralize Truk. I have faith in this squadron and in the United States military forces."

"All right, Padre, I guess this one did affect me more than it should have. When I think of those kids—and that is what they were, just kids—it really hits me; it's a low blow."

Chaplain Richert's Sunday services were always held in the Fifth Group movie theater. Since he was a Protestant he did not conduct a Catholic Mass; that was always held at Thirteenth Air Force headquarters chapel. Attendance at the Protestant service on Sunday mornings was sparse. Out of a squadron of 400 men, it was rare to have more than twenty-five show up for service. On the Sunday after the Wagner crew was listed as missing, the chaplain preached one of his favorite sermons. It was based on the story of Gideon, and Chaplain Reichert tried to make it clear to his small following that the miracles of the Old Testament were symbols of God's will working in our world. He used examples of miraculous events in the very campaign they were fighting to make the point that there were miracles like the one in the Gideon story still happening.

There was a movie at the Fifth Group theater every night after dark. Usually the movie crowd would begin showing up a half hour before it was dark enough to show the movie, so they could get the best seats. While the early arrivers were waiting, the projectionist would play phonograph records just to help pass the time away. The records were seventy-eight RPM and most of them were getting pretty scratchy. One record that was scratchier than the rest was "A Boy and His Horn." In the middle of the record was a dialogue between a female vocalist and the trumpeter, in which the trumpeter enthusiastically shouted that he just had to blow his horn, and the female vocalist replied, "Well, *blow*-oh, Roy, *blow*-oh." Every time that record was played, Major Barlow ranted and raved and told the projectionist to turn it off. It became a game to request the record just to watch Major Barlow act up.

A few days after the Wagner crew had been missing and there was a sort of dull moodiness around the squadron, in the middle of the record session, Chaplain Reichert came on the PA from the projectionist's booth.

"We have had a request from Major Barlow for a special record to be played tonight," he announced. "It took a lot of effort on the part of the projectionist to locate this record. It is a really rare collector's item and shows the high level of Major Barlow's judgment of music that he requested this record. The title of the record is *Roy*."

The major roared and ranted and raved but the record was played and the whole movie amphitheater broke up completely. The group commander, Colonel Everett, was sitting in the top row of the bleacher seats. He looked around at the whole theater rolling with laughter and said to the group operations officer, who was sitting next to him, "We needed that."

The Not-so-Lonely Sea and Sky

June 14, 1944

The first order of business was to repair the leak in the raft occupied by Lieutenant Goerke, Staff Sergeant Musey, Sergeant Whitmore and Corporal Davis. All equipment and supplies in the leaking raft had to be piled into the other raft and then everybody capable of heaving would have to heave it upside down. It took several tries before the feat was accomplished but when the raft was finally upside down, the leak was easily found. Apparently the raft had scraped the coral on the way out through the reef and the rubber coating had been gouged sufficiently to let air leak through the cloth. The raft was left upside down long enough for the area around the scrape to dry in the sun. A patch was taken from the emergency equipment and laid over the scrape. There was some argument as to whether it was necessary to wait for it to dry or harden or set but Staff Sergeant Dotterer had read the instructions. The instructions said that what they were using was a contact cement that set instantly, so the task of turning the raft back over and pumping it back up was soon accomplished. It was easier to inflate than it had been the first time, because by then everyone knew how to accomplish the job.

While the gear was being divided up between the two rafts, the sounds of Japanese Zeros were heard as they approached from Truk. Shortly after the fighters went over at altitudes that were too high to allow them to see the rafts, thirty B-24s were first heard and then seen approaching from the south. An hour and forty-five minutes later, the B-24s were heard and then seen returning. After they were out of sight, the fighters swept in from the south and disappeared in the direction of Truk. It was an unusually clear day for that part of the world.

"Okay, crew, everybody get ready for a swim. We will go in one at a time. The water will make you feel better and will cut down on your drinking water requirements," said Lieutenant Wagner.

"But Lieutenant, I can't swim," Sergeant Whitmore protested.

"That's all right, Sergeant. We'll tie a line on you and pull you in if you lose your grip on the raft."

"What about sharks, Lieutenant?" said Staff Sergeant Dotterer.

"One of us will stand by with an oar whenever there is someone in the water, and if a shark comes close we'll just give him a poke."

One by one, the crew jumped 'skinny' into the ocean and when they returned to the raft, they all had to admit that they felt much better. Even Lieutenant Wagner, with his dislocated shoulder went in. He had to have help getting back on the raft. Staff Sergeant Musey went in very gingerly with his broken wrist. He rolled back in with no trouble, although he had to favor the wrist.

"Tom, isn't it about time for us to hoist the sail and make more speed toward home?" asked Lieutenant Wagner.

"Roger, Jack, but we have got to watch where the wind carried us. Judging by the 24s that went over a while ago, the ocean current is moving us faster than the wind is. We are east of where we should have been if we had had nothing but the trade wind moving us. These rafts don't have keels, and I'm not sure how close we can steer into the wind. I guess we'll just have to give it a try and see how it goes."

Raising the sail took the better part of an hour. Lashing the oars was a problem because there was no way to tell the direction of the blades, and even when the blades were positioned along the length of the raft, they would turn as soon as Lieutenant Bonney tried to steer across the trade wind, making the men's course more south than southwest. Lieutenant Wagner assigned steering watches and Lieutenant Bonney instructed every member how to look at the stars and keep the length of the raft pointed as far east of south as the sail would take wind.

Sundown came and the dark was so dense the men could feel it. The stars were brilliant. The Southern Cross hung like a lantern on the southern horizon. An occasional cloud would obscure it, but the steering watches used it as a guide all night long. At 3:00 A.M. the moon came up. Lieutenant Wagner stirred from his sleep and suddenly sat up when he saw the moon. He gave a sharp cry.

"What is it, Jack?" asked Lieutenant Bonney.

"My shoulder snapped, Tom. I think it just popped back into place!"

"Can you move your arm?"

"Yep. It's stiff and sore, but I think it's usable again."

"Good news, Jack. See if you can get some more sleep."

Planning for Survival

June 15, 1944

"Tom, how far do you think we've sailed so far?" Lieutenant Wagner asked Lieutenant Bonney.

"I'm not sure, Jack. We haven't seen any bombers today; in fact, we haven't seen any airplanes at all. I don't know whether we've drifted too far off the flight path or if there just wasn't a mission today. The trouble is that we're sailing toward the southwest but the current is toward the east, and I don't know which is pushing us the hardest. In any case, there are no islands to speak of between Truk and Mokerang. If we are drifting and sailing southwest—which I suspect, because we were west of the bomber flight path yesterday—there are no islands until we get to New Guinea, and that's over a thousand miles away."

"How long will it take us to get there?"

"If we are really averaging five miles per hour, which is just a guess, we are traveling 120 miles per day. At that rate, we should be there in less than ten days. I'm worried, though, because all of that area is in Japanese hands. If we land on the coast of New Guinea we are going to be captured for sure. If we get close to New Guinea, we are sure to be picked up by a Japanese search plane."

"Should we put out a sea anchor and let the current take us farther east?"

"No, I don't think that's such a good idea, Jack, because

the current doesn't flow directly east, it is sort of east-northeast, and that will take us right back to the vicinity of Truk. We stand a chance of being captured there too."

"Okay, Tom," Lieutenant Wagner said, sounding resigned. "I guess we better keep on sailing and hope we can see some airplanes that will give us a feeling for our course."

"Everybody! Listen up! Tom is estimating that we will be out here for at least seven more days, so I want everyone to keep an eye out for airplanes that might give us a clue as to our position. Whoever is steering, keep it as near south as possible. Tom tells me that we are drifting too far west and that if we keep it up, we will be in an area that the Japanese control, where we would stand a good chance of being captured. We've had good luck collecting water so far, but that doesn't say that we will be that lucky every day. I want you to split the tops of most of the life jackets and fill them with water when we do catch some. Save a couple of life jackets for those who can't swim. Also, let's take turns on that fish net and get some dried fish laid out. Our emergency food stores won't last seven days."

Staff Sergeant Musey exercised his broken wrist continually. It was very painful, but he moved it as much as he could and massaged it with his left hand.

There were sharks around the rafts all the time. Most of them were small, the so-called "dog sharks" that were mostly after the small fish that hid under the rafts to keep out of the sun, but one shark was bigger than the rest. The crew finally named him Ole Man Moe. He had all the other sharks and small fish spooked, so that while he was around there was nothing else in the area. As night fell, Ole Man Moe kept coming up and rubbing against the rafts. He was disturbing everyone who was trying to sleep. Staff Sergeant Rokos woke up when Ole Man Moe rubbed the raft right under where he was sleeping. Rokos reached over the side of the raft and felt the dorsal fin of Ole Man Moe. He grabbed the fin and shook it. Ole Man Moe took off like a scalded cat, and didn't come back that night.

About midnight, the sea began to "freshen." That's sailor talk that means the waves were getting bigger and bigger. It was hard to sleep when every fifteen seconds or so the rafts were riding up on the crest of a wave and then taking a shuddering dive down to the trough.

Seasick Time

June 16, 1944

By morning the waves had grown to thirty feet from crest to trough. Even though all of the crew had flown many hours through rough weather, this was different. The constant run up to the crest of a wave and then the sickening plunge down to the trough every fifteen seconds unsettled even the sturdiest stomachs.

"Who's doing the lookout duty?" Lieutenant Wagner shouted above the sound of the cresting waves. A few heads rose slightly, but there was no enthusiasm.

"Chuck, do you have anybody in your raft who can take lookout duty?" Lieutenant Wagner queried Lieutenant Goerke.

"Jack, none of us can hold our heads up, let alone look around. I feel as bad as any of them."

"Okay Chuck, Tom and I will try to keep and eye out, but neither one of us feels much like it, either."

Somehow, lying down and hanging on to the rafts made everyone feel a little more like living. The act of looking out at the horizon while the rafts were pitching and tossing in the waves eventually caused stomach turmoil. Lieutenant Wagner and Lieutenant Bonney traded off watch most of the day. As soon as one of them reached the limit of nausea, the other would take over. Their routine paid off.

Near noon, Lieutenant Wagner spotted a Japanese airplane flying very low. The sail was quickly lowered and the camouflage cloth was raised to keep the Japanese crew from seeing them. It was remarkable how men who could hardly raise their heads one minute could perform certain activities a minute later when those activities were necessary for their survival. The airplane was recognized as a 'Nell.' It was probably on a reconnaissance mission.

"Tom, what do you make of the course of that Nell?" asked Lieutenant Wagner.

"Jack, the course he was flying doesn't make any sense at all. Either we are closer to Truk than I thought we would be by now, or he is flying out of some other atoll; maybe Woleai. If he is out of Woleai we are really west of our course back to Mokerang."

"Should we change our route?"

"No, I think we should keep sailing the way we have been. If we are west of course, maybe one of our Snooper searches along the north coast of New Guinea will spot us before the Japs do."

"Okay Crew! Hoist the sail and let's try to steer as near south as we can. Lieutenant Bonney tells me we are a long way west of course."

In spite of the heavy sea, the crew had the sail up in short order. Then they all went back to nursing their nausea.

The daily dip in the ocean was a real challenge with the heavy sea, but Lieutenant Wagner insisted that every man take a dip. Even Sergeant Whitmore went in. It was also a challenge to keep the inside of the rafts bailed out so that the men's skins did not become soaked all the time. Lieutenant Walker and Lieutenant Goerke used every method, from military order to cajolery, to keep the rafts reasonably dry. Almost every wave slopped some water into the rafts and it took constant bailing to keep them reasonably dry.

By the end of the day, most of the crew had gotten over the nausea, but they were all weak. Nobody felt like standing watch or taking a steering turn.

"Tom, what do you think about taking down the sail and just drifting tonight? Everybody is too tired to steer and I'm not sure that steering really gets us anywhere."

"I'll have to agree, Jack. Maybe if we all get some rest we can make for a better course tomorrow; also, I'm hoping this sea will subside a little."

"Okay, Tom. Crew! Take down the sail, we are going to drift tonight and hope we will be feeling better tomorrow! I still want a rotating watch, but we can go with one-hour watches, alternating between the two rafts. Chuck, you take the first hour and call me when it is up."

"Roger, Jack. What should we do if we see a light or an airplane?"

"We have the Gibson Girl; whoever is on watch should have it ready to crank. Signal with the light."

The "Gibson Girl" was a unit with a hand crank generator that had a signal light and a radio transmitter that automatically sent an SOS signal on the emergency frequency. If there was a qualified radio operator present, he could operate the unit's Morse code key to send a message to whoever was within receiving distance.

The sail was lowered and everyone except Lieutenant Goerke settled down to try and get some sleep. Lowering the sail also seemed to reduce the water that was being splashed into the bottom of the rafts.

Lieutenant Goerke took the first watch and called Lieutenant Wagner at 9:00 P.M. Lieutenant Wagner took the watch until 10:00, when he called Staff Sergeant Musey. At 11:00 Staff Sergeant Musey called Lieutenant Bonney. Lieutenant Bonney took one look around and called Lieutenant Wagner.

"Jack, it just cleared up and I got a good look at the Southern Cross. We are definitely moving south. It is about four degrees higher above the horizon than it was that first clear night out of Truk. Four degrees is only 280 miles, though, so either we are really drifting southwest or we are going half as fast as I estimated."

"Let's hope that this drifting without a sail doesn't carry us too far back toward Truk, Tom. I would hate for us to be spotted by a Japanese sea search now."

"I'll try to get another look at the Southern Cross tomorrow night and see if we are making any progress to the south, Jack. I sure wish I could have saved my octant. Get back to sleep and I'll talk to you in the morning."

Empty Sea

June 17, 1944

Sunrise caught everyone by surprise—everyone except Staff Sergeant Rokos. He had had the last duty hour of the night and had felt the waves recede and seen the eastern sky turn pink and then red. The sea had become almost calm, especially when compared to the pitching and tossing of the night before. Lieutenant Wagner called for the sail to be erected, and watches were set to try to steer the rafts south again. Staff Sergeant Musey nursed his broken wrist.

"How is the wrist doing?" Lieutenant Goerke asked him.

"It's getting better, Lieutenant. I keep working it as far as I can before the pain stops me, and I can move it farther every day."

Staff Sergeant Musey had been dipping up fish from under the raft before the high waves came along and now he got out the net and began dipping small fish out again. Most of the fish he caught with the net were smelt. They were only a few inches long, but Corporal Davis cleaned them and sliced them down the middle and laid them out on the edge of the raft where they dried. Nobody really raved about the taste, but nobody complained, either.

Staff Sergeant Musey found some fishing tackle in the emergency stores and tried using it, baiting it with pieces of the smelt he had dipped up. The first fish he caught was a baby shark. Nobody knew what to do with it. They finally threw it back into the ocean. After discussion it was decided that the small sharks were actually helping them, because whenever they came around, the small fish tried to hide under the raft and whoever had the net could scoop them up.

Ole Man Moe returned in the middle of the morning. The oar patrol had to be reactivated while the crew's skinny dip into the ocean was in progress. Lieutenant Wagner divided the watches into groups of two so that one man on watch could operate the oar that was being used as a tiller while the other held another oar, lashed onto the side of the raft to act as a keel. It didn't work. Many times the man on the tiller would try to steer across the trade wind. Every time the raft would start to come around it would fall off course again as soon as the wind hit. It took a lot of energy on the part of the watch to try to bring the rafts into the wind and see them fall off time after time. Lieutenant Bonney was sure that they would probably make more headway if they just ran with the wind, but he was still worried about where the wind would take them.

"Jack, have you noticed that there aren't any birds?" Lieutenant Bonney asked Lieutenant Wagner.

"What do you mean, Tom?"

"Well, before we went through the high waves, there always seemed to be sea gulls or albatross around, but since it calmed down I haven't seen bird one."

"I hadn't noticed, Tom, but now that you mentioned it, you're right. I haven't seen a bird all day. Get out your map and let's see if we can figure out why."

Tom pulled his map out of the waterproof folder and they spread it out on the side of the raft.

"Oh, I see, Jack. We have drifted into the East Caroline basin. It doesn't make any difference whether we have been moving south-southwest or just plain southwest, we would still be in the basin and there are no islands for hundreds of miles. Those waves we went through must have been at the edge of the basin. The reason we haven't seen any birds is because we're too far from land."

"What does that tell you about our position and direction of travel?"

"Not much, Jack. The East Caroline Basin is so big that we could be anywhere within a 500-mile diameter circle. If we run into another area of high waves, that will probably be the other side of the basin. If that happens, we should make a careful assessment of the wave direction. That may tell us where we are."

"So, what do we do in the meantime? Just drift along and hope someone friendly spots us?"

"That's about it, Jack. I don't know what else to suggest."

Ole Man Moe rubbed against the raft Lieutenant Goerke was in.

"Sergeant Whitmore, take one of the oars and bash that sucker. I'm getting tired of him," said Lieutenant Goerke.

Sergeant Whitmore unlashed one of the oars and looked over the side for Ole Man Moe, but he was gone. Sergeant Whitmore lashed the oar back on to the raft when Ole Man Moe rubbed against the raft again. Sergeant Whitmore unlashed the oar but again, when he looked for Ole Man Moe the shark was gone. This time, Sergeant Whitmore waited. Sure enough, in about five minutes, Ole Man Moe was back, and as he rubbed against the raft, Sergeant Whitmore gave him a poke with the oar. Ole Man Moe took off at full speed and didn't return for at least fifteen minutes. Then it became a game. Sergeant Whitmore would wait until Ole Man Moe rubbed against the raft and then he would get ready for the next time, which would be about five minutes later. When Ole Man Moe reappeared, Sergeant Whitmore would give him a poke with the oar. It was a game that could have lasted all day, but Sergeant Whitmore became tired of wielding the heavy oar and nobody else wanted to take over. Even Lieutenant Goerke lost interest.

There were no sightings all day. Several rain showers passed across the rafts and all hands were used to hold anything that could collect water. The men filled every receptacle that would hold fresh water. The life vests had been split and water was poured into them. Later, when the water in the life vests was used for drinking, everyone made faces and complained about the taste of the powder that had been in the vests to keep them from sticking together in the equatorial weather. Even after they had been used several times for storing rain water the vests still had the taste of the powder.

More Empty Sea

June 18, 19, and 20, 1944

The ocean was empty. The sky was empty. Nothing seemed to move. There was a gentle sea, swells about three feet from crest to trough with a period of twelve seconds. According to the compass that Lieutenant Bonney had dug out of the emergency equipment, the wind was directly out of the northeast, very gentle, about seven miles per hour. An occasional cumulus cloud blew over and dropped a shower on the rafts. Everybody knew automatically that they should get out the cloths or jackets or whatever they used to catch the rain and store it in the canvas buckets or in the life jackets that had been ripped open.

The steering watches were ordered by Lieutenant Wagner. The rest of the crew kept a lookout on the horizon whenever they were awake. Staff Sergeant Musey kept working his wrist, which was almost back to normal, although it was stiff and sore in some positions, and he showed it off every time he noticed that he had more flexibility than before. He even shifted the fish net to his right hand and caught fish with it. He caught so many small fish that between his netting and Corporal Davis cutting and drying so many small fish, they finally ran out of drying space on the rims of the rafts. Daily swims were ordered by Lieutenant Wagner and the supply of vitamin pills was carefully rationed to be sure that everyone got one every day.

On June 20, Lieutenant Goerke called over to Lieutenant Bonney, "Hey, Tom, I thought you said that we would be in

New Guinea by now. What happened?"

"I don't know, Chuck. I think the equatorial current has had more effect on the rafts than I thought it would. I guess we are not the best sailors in the world, either. I know that we have not been following the course that would get us to Mokerang, but we must be off by more than I thought."

"Chuck, I think we should be thankful that we are still alive and kicking," Lieutenant Wagner interjected. "I know that we must be in a part of the ocean that has very little ship activity and therefore the snoopers and the U.S. Navy don't even assign sea-search missions out here. If they did, we would have been picked up before now. If we keep going in the same direction that we have been for the last ten days, we are going to drift into a more active part of the world and we *will* be picked up. I just hope it is by the U.S. and not the Japanese."

"Amen," came from Lieutenant Goerke.

East Caroline Basin

Just as there are deserts on land, there are deserts on the ocean. The ecology of the ocean is vastly complex. There are many interconnections between the surface fish and plants and deep water fish and plants. The algae that produce oxygen for the water and eventually for the air we breathe can live only in shallow water. At about one hundred feet depth, there is not enough sunlight to allow the algae to grow. In normal open sea and along continental shelves, the algae grow and die and the debris from their corpses slowly sinks to the bottom and produces a silt that the bottom feeders live on. Over the whole surface of the earth, the rate of growth of the silt averages about ten centimeters in one hundred years. Of course there are areas of the ocean where the accumulation of silt is much slower, sometimes so slow that it is immeasurable. The East Caroline Basin is one of those areas.

The bottom of the East Caroline Basin is a vast plane almost one thousand miles across. The depth of the plane is more than a mile (it averages about twelve hundred fathoms) and doesn't vary more than one hundred fathoms over the whole area. The East Caroline Basin is geologically very old. It is the oldest area in the whole Pacific Ocean, having been extant for more than one hundred fifty million years.

Because of the depth of water in the basin, kelp and other ocean plants that grow from the ocean floor and reach up for sunlight cannot exist in the basin. Therefore small fish and snails and starfish and sea urchins cannot survive, and the chain that grows from these lower forms to game fish and sharks has no basis for growth. Generally, if game fish accidentally wander into the basin, they either starve to death or they get out and migrate to more well-populated areas.

The weather over the basin also hinders the growth of a food base. The wind is generally light and blows counter to the equatorial trade wind. The result of this wind condition is that very little insect debris is carried to the basin, because any insect that reached the basin would have had to be in the air all the way from South America.

The vast size of the basin is a deterrent to any bird life. Not only are the distances to land masses vast, but the schools of fish that albatross and seagulls feed on when they are at sea just do not exist in the basin. In ancient times, the Polynesians shunned the East Caroline Basin because their ballads of the sea warned against sailing into this wilderness.

A Friendly

June 21, 1944

The routine was pretty well set by this time. The watches were assigned. Everyone looked out at the horizon when they were not resting or steering or netting small fish or skinny dipping. Staff Sergeant Musey's wrist was practically as good as new. Everyone was so sunburned that they looked like a group of natives.

"If it wasn't for the rafts giving us away," Lieutenant Goerke remarked, "we could all pose as Micronesians and the Japanese wouldn't know the difference. Can any of you speak Malaysian? Maybe we ought to practice just in case we run into unfriendlies."

"What makes you think the Japanese will see us first, Chuck?" asked Lieutenant Bonney.

"I figure that as far off as you are on our position, we might end up in Java, Tom."

"Chuck, if we end up in Java, I'll give you first chance at the first dancing girl we see."

"I figure she would pick me anyway, Tom."

At noon, Staff Sergeant Dotterer, who was on watch, spotted a PBY (Catalina flying boat). Instantly everyone in the crew was on their feet, waving everything they could wave that might attract the attention of the crew. The sun was behind a cumulus cloud, so the rescue mirror was useless. The Catalina kept to its original course and in fifteen minutes she disappeared from sight.

114

The whole crew was discouraged. At the same time the men were aware that they were entering a part of the ocean that was being scanned by the navy.

"Tom, what course was that cat on?" Lieutenant Wagner wanted to know.

"According to my compass, he was flying a course of 300 degrees, Jack. If he took off from Mokerang or Momote, he must have been in the air for six or seven hours. If he is flying search, he should turn left and fly for about an hour and then go back to his home base. That will put him too far south to see us on his way back."

"I wonder if we are in an area where they make daily searches," said Lieutenant Wagner.

"I can't believe that he was on some kind of random search, Jack. We should keep a sharp lookout about this same time tomorrow. We will have sailed about sixty miles by then if we keep the sail up, so I suggest that we lower the sail and see if we can keep near enough to this location that we can see him tomorrow. Maybe the sun will be out then, and we can flash him with the rescue mirror."

"That sounds like a good idea, Tom. All right, Crew! Take down the sail and let's drift until tomorrow. Hopefully we will see the cat again and can signal to him."

The sail was taken down and the oars were lashed to the rafts. The crew prepared to wait for twenty-four hours. It would be a long, nervous twenty-four hours.

Back to the Lonely Sea

June 22, 1944

It was more overcast than it had been for a week. The ceiling was about 4,000 feet and there was intermittent rain all day. The whole crew was watching anxiously for some sign of the Catalina flying boat, but strain their eyes as they might, there was no sign. It rained occasionally, sometimes for a half hour at a time. They all knew that if the Catalina came by while it was raining, there would be no chance of them hearing it over the sound of the pelting rain. The only reason they wanted to hear it would be to confirm that it was on a daily search; then they'd know they might have a chance of being seen. The men also knew that they couldn't hope for help from the PBY unless the weather cleared up so they could see the sun at the same time that they saw the search plane.

"What do you think, Tom? Should we put the sail back up?" Lieutenant Wagner asked Lieutenant Bonney.

"Since you asked me what I think, Jack, I think we should stay as close as possible to the spot where we originally saw the cat."

"Well, Okay, but how far are we drifting with the sail down?"

"According to the map, we should be drifting about fifty miles per day—sort of easterly, if I can believe the map."

"One thing I have been worried about, Tom, is the course that the cat was on. If he was flying a normal sea-search pattern, he would be on his most northerly and easterly leg. Of course, we have to assume that he was on a search pattern and not just on a special mission of some sort. If we continue to drift easterly, we may just drift out of his search pattern. I have no idea where the next search pattern is east of here."

"Let's give it one more day, and then if we don't see him again we can hoist the sail."

"Hey, Chuck!" Lieutenant Wagner called to Lieutenant Goerke, "We are going to drift for one more day and see if the cat goes by again. If he doesn't, we'll hoist the sail and try to sail south again."

"I think we're pounding sand, Jack, but if that's what you want to do, it's okay by me. We certainly aren't hurting for food or water, and it looks like we can continue for a long time if we don't get caught at it—by the Japanese, that is."

Extra watch was posted for the night, which passed very slowly. The overcast sky made it dark even though there was a new moon lighting the backs of the clouds after the sun went down. Nothing was sighted.

Sailing Again

June 23, 1944

Everyone in the crew strained their eyes and ears all day for a sign of the Catalina. By late afternoon, Lieutenant Bonney and Lieutenant Wagner realized that if the Catalina had been searching in the area it would be on its way home by then.

"Tom, I'm going to have the sail erected again," Lieutenant Wagner said to Lieutenant Bonney.

"Sure, Jack, maybe we will sail into a search pattern."

"Crew! Let's get the sail back up, and let's go back to the original watches with one man steering and one trying to keep the keel oar straight," called Lieutenant Wagner.

One more night of trying to sail: The old problem of trying to keep the keel oar straight was back again. The steersman would try to come left to steer south and when the side load came up on the keel oar it would twist out of the lashings or even twist out of the hands of the man who was trying to hold it steady, and the rafts would slew around until the sail lost its wind. Then the whole operation would be repeated. It seemed that the sea was plotting against them.

June 24 came and went. Often the men would just run before the breeze, knowing that it was carrying them closer to Japanese-held islands north of New Guinea. The next two days no better. The amazing thing about the whole ordeal was that there were no arguments, no infighting. Every member of the crew realized that if they were going to survive they would have to work together.

The sun rose on June 27 to clear skies, the first in several days. Because of the cloudy skies, the small fish had not been seeking the shadow of the rafts, and the supply of dried fish on the edge of the rafts was almost depleted. With the coming of the sun, the fish returned, and Staff Sergeant Musey was back pulling them out with the net while his partner, Corporal Davis, dressed them to dry in the sun. Staff Sergeant Musey's wrist was completely healed, although it appeared to be somewhat swollen from the scar tissue around the break.

At noon, a Catalina flying boat appeared on the northern horizon. The whole crew was up waving flight jackets, jump suits, pieces of cloth: anything they thought would attract attention. The Catalina never varied its course or gave any indication that it had detected them. The signaling mirror either wasn't being used properly or—for some reason—the signal was just not being seen by the crew of the cat.

"Tom, what course is he making?" Lieutenant Wagner asked Lieutenant Bonney.

"Close to 300 degrees again, Jack. We are seeing him earlier than the first sighting and we are on the other side of his course. I really think we should take down the sail now and see if we can drift closer to his outbound search leg."

"Okay—Crew! Take down the sail and keep a careful watch," ordered Lieutenant Wagner, "We must be close to regularly scheduled search patterns."

Like a Blind Horse

June 28, 1944

The Catalina appeared before noon. They were closer to his flight course and everyone again waved anything they could wave to try to attract attention. No luck. The cat flew on as if they didn't exist. Lieutenant Bonney used the rescue mirror, but there was no sign that the crew in the cat had seen it. By this time, there were two attitudes in the rafts; the optimists were sure that they would be found by friendly search planes, and the pessimists were sure that they would still be floating in the rafts by Christmas.

"I think those guys are either blind or they have one heck of a card game going up there," grumbled Lieutenant Goerke.

"Aw, don't be too rough on them, Chuck. You know how small we are out here in the middle of the ocean."

"Tom, do you think we should sail some more or should we keep on drifting with the current?"

"I think we should keep drifting, Jack. We're closer to his flight path than we have ever been and I'm afraid that if we put up the sail, it will carry us too far south."

It was another tense twenty-four hours.

June 29 was another clear day. The Catalina appeared even earlier than it had before. It was on the same 300-degree course and the men thought that maybe they were a little closer to the flight path, but maybe that was just wishful thinking. Lieutenant Bonney signaled with the mirror from the time the cat appeared until it was out of sight. Again, no luck. Lieutenant Wagner and Lieutenant Bonney and Lieutenant Goerke put their heads together and tried to make some sense out of the sightings. They were convinced that the cat probably came by on some of the days that they did not see it and that only the weather and poor visibility kept them from seeing it sometimes. The plain facts were that they could see the cat, but the cat couldn't see them. The men were limited in what they could do to attract attention, and they could only hope that finally they would end up close enough to the flight path of the cat's search pattern that they would be seen.

They decided to drift again.

The haze created by a half-moon made it difficult to see any stars at all. The watches didn't know which direction they were looking, but they looked anyway. After midnight, when the moon had gone down and the stars were visible again, Staff Sergeant Rokos, who was on watch, called Lieutenant Wagner and told him that he was seeing lights in the distance on the surface.

All of the crew woke up and began watching the lights. After some discussion, it was decided that they should break out the Gibson Girl and try to flash a message in the direction of the lights. The Gibson Girl was useless for radio messages, and had been the whole time they were in the water, because the kite kit and balloon kit had been lost during the water landing. The Gibson Girl would be able to flash a light message though.

The Gibson Girl was unlashed from the edge of the raft where it had been since the water landing, and Staff Sergeant Rokos began cranking the generator. Nothing happened. The signal light didn't come on. In spite of everything the men did, hampered as they were by the dark, nothing would make the light work. All to soon the distant lights went out.

Rescue at Last

June 30, 1944

Navy Lt. Fred Hough was the pilot of the 300-degree search out of Momote in the Catalina. The copilot was Lt. (JG) Andrew Post. There were five other crewmen on board. Their mission was to look for Japanese submarines. On previous missions in the area they had had little luck finding anything that even looked like a submarine in that part of the ocean. Mostly they relied on the ASV radar to find a periscope so they could home in on it and drop one of their retro depth charges as they passed over the sub, but periscopes give a very faint return on an ASV and, in any case, there were very few sightings in the East Caroline Basin.

They had taken off from Momote at 0600 hours that day, and by 1000 they had reported no sightings back to base. Lieutenant Hough had to make a head run and as soon as the negative message was acknowledged by base, he left the flight deck with Lieutenant (JG) Post in command of the aircraft. Lieutenant (JG) Post was looking out the right window of the flight deck to see if there were any clouds around. He was flying at 5,000 feet, small cumulus clouds often built up at that altitude. Out of the corner of his eye, Post caught a flash and asked the assistant engineer to bring him a set of binoculars from the observation windows in the waist.

As soon as he scanned the ocean with the binoculars in the direction of the glint he had seen, Post spotted the rafts and called Lieutenant Hough. Lieutenant Hough immediately turned toward the rafts and, since the ocean was almost calm, he landed beside them and took the eight Snoopers on board. Lieutenant Hough also called in to base as soon as they were back in the air and reported the rescue. He requested permission to return directly to base. Permission was granted. By afternoon the eight survivors were in the 58th Evacuation Hospital.

Snooper Mess Hall

June 30, 1944

Capt. Vince Splane was about to take on some chow before the evening briefing. The duty sergeant came up to him and said, "Captain Splane, the navy wants to talk to you on the telephone."

Captain Splane went to the orderly room and picked up the phone. The voice on the other end said, "Captain, we have one of your crews over here, led by a Lt. Jack Wagner."

All eight men were in remarkably good shape. They had used the vitamin pills to supplement their diets, they had kept clean with their daily dips in the ocean, and the fish diet had not hurt them at all. Staff Sergeant Musey had his wrist X-rayed. It had healed perfectly. Lieutenant Wagner's shoulder was completely healed. The only physical trauma that they all were suffering from was sunburn.

All eight crewmen were returned to the United States for re-assignment.

Disaster at Thanksgiving

It was traditional in WWII that all services would supply turkeys for a good old-fashioned Thanksgiving dinner whenever it was possible. Thanksgiving 1944 found the Snoopers on Noemfoor Island. Turkeys were flown in from Australia and the cooks prepared a feast. In addition to baked turkeys,they had fixed mashed potatoes, three kinds of vegetables, cranberries, and, as a final flourish, fresh-baked pumpkin pies. It was a welcome change from the usual dehydrated stuff that comprised the day-to-day fare that took so much ridicule from troops in combat situations. Of course, it is also a good old-fashioned tradition that at any Thanksgiving feast everyone overeats. So it was that on Thanksgiving day in 1944, the Snoopers dug in and fulfilled the tradition.

An hour after the first shift had finished their feast, they began to realize that their stomachs were in turmoil. Since the shifts were each a half-hour long, by the time the first shift was experiencing their malaise, the second shift had finished eating and the third shift was well into their meal. By evening 500 men of the 868th Squadron were going through the trauma of food poisoning. The flight surgeon was overwhelmed by requests for a remedy for stomach cramps, nausea, diarrhea, and physical weakness. The flight surgeon was as sick as everyone else. His corpsmen were sick. The whole squadron was a disaster area.

The latrines were the most populated centers, but they were not designed to handle a run like the one that happened

Thanksgiving night. The problem was that men who headed for the latrines couldn't wait in a line. This situation was the ultimate proof of the adage, "When you gotta go, you gotta go!" The latrines were all screened in to keep the insects out as much as possible. Sgt. Vince Hoover was in one of the latrines in the middle of the night. He had been there off and on most of the night. Finally he decided to go back to his tent and try to get some sleep. As he opened the door and stepped outside, Cpl. Jerry Sisson was coming down the path at a dead run. The men collided in the doorway. Corporal Sisson said resignedly, "Oh, well, I guess I wouldn't have made it anyway."

There was one fatality. Leo Feldman, bombardier, became violently ill in the afternoon, and although the medics rushed him to the hospital, he died enroute.

Capt. Robert Wallace at Tarakan

Capt. Robert Wallace was trained as a P-38 fighter pilot. During his tour of duty at Los Negros he contracted a fungus infection in his ears which made it virtually impossible for him to fly fighter mission in his P-38. Because the Snoopers flew mostly low-altitude missions, he was transferred from Thirteenth Fighter Command to Thirteenth Bomber Command and assigned to the Snoopers.

The Snoopers had moved again. This time they had been moved to Noemfoor Island in the northeast corner of Geelvink Bay on the north side of New Guinea. The missions were even more demanding than the missions they had been flying out of Mokerang. They were ordered to search for ships in the Celebes Sea, but there was very little shipping to be found, even with the Snooper radar, and the only way the Snoopers could cover the designated area was to stage out of Morotai in the Halmahera Islands. Most of the missions ended with the bombs being dropped on some remote outpost of the Japanese army or navy—some island or other that had been bypassed by the Allied advance.

It was a frustrating time for all the Snoopers, but it was especially frustrating for Captain Wallace. He was scheduled to search for shipping in the Celebes Sea on his third mission. He knew and the briefing officer knew that there was zero shipping in the Celebes Sea; the Snoopers had wiped it out long before. His first two missions had resulted in bombs being dumped on some miserable Japanese outposts that had been all but abandoned by the Japanese—some out-of-the-way islands on the periphery of the sea.

Captain Wallace pulled a stunt that could have cost him his commission in the air corps. He sneaked into the intelligence tent when no one was around and picked up a set of aerial photographs of Tarakan Island. The photographs showed twenty-five miles of oil wells, oil refinery units, and storage tanks at Lutong. This installation had been ignored by General Matheny due to the pressure of supporting the invasion of the Philippines, but the Lutong complex was extremely valuable to the Japanese because the crude oil that came out of the ground could go right into the bunkers of the Japanese submarines with very little refining.

Captain Wallace was pissed at the Japanese anyway, because when he had been preparing for his third mission and was about to take off from Morotai, the Japanese had pulled a surprise air raid and wounded two of his crew members. The incident delayed his mission from November 23 to December 7.

Morotai—December 7, 1944—1730 Hours

Radio traffic:

"Pitoe Tower, this is air force *955* Request permission to taxi and takeoff."

"Roger, *955* You are cleared for takeoff on runway 2-8."

Intercom conversation on *955:*

"Crew, this is Captain Wallace. Prepare for takeoff. Check list complete. Give me full military power." He paused. "We're on our way."

Aircraft *955* was named *Lucky Lady*. She was one of the newest Snooper aircraft, but with full wing tanks, two bomb-bay tanks topped off and a load of sixteen 250-pound general purpose bombs, *Lucky Lady* was on full military power for seven minutes before Captain Wallace could lower the nose and put the aircraft into level flight at 2,500 feet altitude. He trimmed the plane and engaged the Minneapolis-Honeywell autopilot, waited a few minutes, and then spoke into the intercom:

"All crew members, report to the flight deck."

Getting the normal ten crew members to the flight deck was a struggle, but on this mission there was an eleventh man. He was a Paramount Pictures news cameraman. Somehow most of the crew squeezed up on the flight deck, stood in the walkway to the bomb bay, or listened to the intercom. Captain Wallace shouted above the noise of the engines (which were still pulling more than normal cruise power, since there had not been enough time elapsed to burn off a significant weight of fuel):

"Crew, I am not going to waste this load of bombs on some deserted Jap outpost in the middle of nowhere. I want you all to take a look at these pictures that I picked up from the S-2 [squadron intelligence] tent. They show the oil refinery at Lutong, which hasn't been touched by a U.S. Bombing raid. If we don't see a ship we are going to give them a surprise tomorrow morning. I want all of you to take a good look at the pictures and be able to identify important targets in that particular area of Lutong. The bombardier will put our bombs on the refinery and the rest of you can shoot at any and all of the tanks in the surrounding tank farms. Our Paramount News cameraman will record the event for posterity. Just to make you feel better, we are going across the installation at 100 feet altitude. That should give the antiaircraft gun crews the smallest chance to get a shot at us. When you have had a chance to look at the pictures, return to your flight stations. Stay on the intercom. That's all."

The search of the Celebes Sea was fruitless. From Morotai, Captain Wallace took a heading of 270 degrees. By 1900 hours he passed the long north-south stretch of the Moluccas, which looked like a string of beads connecting the north tip of Celebes Island with the south tip of Mindanao. He turned to a heading of 250 degrees for the next half hour to allow the radar to scan the long east-west sweep of the north arm of Celebes. Wallace knew that the thousands of coves and estuaries along that 300 miles of coast could hide hundreds of Sugar-Charlies, but he also knew that the Japanese coast watcher in the hills above Pitoe Airfield had sent a message to the Japanese naval command that he was on his way, and that that particular night would be a good night for the Sugar-Charlies to hide out. When the radar showed that he was twenty-five miles from the coast he turned back to 270 and waited for a call from the radar operator letting him know there was a target in sight.

By 2000 hours, twilight had ended. A half moon rose behind *Lucky Lady,* lighting up the sea when clouds cleared away. At 2200 hours, Makassar Strait opened up around the curve of Celebes and Captain Wallace turned to 330 degrees to search up to the Sulu Archipelago.

It was mostly open sea for the next two hours. Occasionally one of the long capes of Borneo would appear at the edge of the radar screen, but mostly it was an empty ocean. At 2400 hours, Captain Wallace made a gradual right turn, which took him up the chain of the Sulu Archipelago. The myriad of little islands kept the radar screen so cluttered that there was no sense in trying to find a ship of any size in the mess. At 0400 hours, Captain Wallace spoke over the intercom:

"Navigator, this is the pilot. Give me a course to Tarakan."

"Roger, Bob. Take a course of 225 degrees. I'll keep track of our position. We should see the island on the radar just before sunrise."

"Roger, Gus. I want to get there when there is enough light for us to see what we are doing, but I don't want the Japs to be too bright eyed and bushy tailed."

"Radar, this is the pilot."

"Radar. Roger."

"Radar, when we are in sight of Tarakan, I want you to shut down the radar, pull up the radome, and get on one of the waist guns. I want everything on this airplane that can throw bullets to throw them. Do you understand?"

"Roger. Willco, Captain."

On a normal Snooper mission, only one waist gunner was carried, but there were two waist guns, one out of each side of the aircraft. Captain Wallace did not want an idle gun while they were attacking the oil field installations at Lutong. He asked the radar operator to pull up the radome so the aircraft would be as clean as possible; with a cleaned-up aircraft, the flying speed would be higher without requiring excessive engine power.

0600 Hours

"Navigator to pilot."

"Roger, Gus. Go ahead."

"Bob, I have a fix on Tarakan Island. It is seventy miles at 220 degrees. Do you want to make landfall on the north or south end of the island?"

"Lutong is on the north end of the island, Gus. I would like to pass over the beach about the middle of the island so I can make a right turn and see Lutong in front of us."

"Roger, Bob. Hold this heading and you will just about cut the island in half."

"Radar, this is the pilot. When the beach is at fifty miles range, shut down the radar, crank up the radome and man one of the waist guns."

"Radar. Roger."

The nose turret gunner, the top turret gunner, the tail gunner and the waist gunner each charged their guns and fired a short burst of two rounds to verify that they were all working. Captain Wallace was still flying at optimum cruise engine power. Ten minutes passed.

"Pilot, this is Radar. I have fifty miles range to the beach. Radar is going off."

"Roger, Radar."

Just behind the waist windows, where the waist gunner's swivel-mounted fifty-caliber machine guns stuck out into the slipstream, there were small Plexiglas windows. The newsreel cameraman took a position by the window on the left side of the airplane. Captain Wallace had been flying at an altitude of 3,000 feet. When the radar operator called out fifty miles range, he trimmed the nose down and slowly descended to 500 feet altitude. At 0645 hours the sun came up behind *Lucky Lady* and the tops of the hills beyond Tarakan Island turned red, then yellow, and then green. Shadows were creeping down the hills and, as they crossed the beach, sunlight flooded Tarakan Island.

"Pilot to crew: Hang on, I'm going to see how fast this *Lucky Lady* can go."

Captain Wallace made a right turn and flew up the beach.

"Copilot, give me thirty five inches and 2,500 *RPM.*"

"Roger, Bob: Thirty-five twenty-five."

"Bombardier, get ready to drop all bombs on the refinery."

"Roger, Bob. I'll drop them all with twenty five foot spacing."

"Pilot to crew: I have the refinery in sight. Get ready to strafe and bomb."

"Roger," replied the bombardier and all gunners.

Captain Wallace lowered the nose and let the radar altimeter sink from 500 feet to 200 feet and then, as they passed over the refinery, to 100 feet. The nose turret was the first to erupt. Fifty-caliber rounds and tracers pounded into oil storage tanks. The bombardier recognized the cracking plant from the photographs and he put all sixteen 250-pound bombs along the length of the plant. Waist gunners were firing at oil storage tanks on each side of the flight path. The tail gunner was watching for any tanks that were not on fire when they came into his field of view; he poured more fifty-caliber rounds and tracers into them.

"Pilot to crew: Hold your fire, there are lots more storage tanks ahead of us, wait until you see a target before you fire."

"Pilot to top turret: Save your ammo, I have a couple of targets for you."

"Top Turret. Roger."

Captain Wallace made six strafing runs on the oil tanks north of Lutong.

"Top Turret, get ready; there is a Japanese Betty on the airfield at Miri just to the west of the refinery. I'm going to bank around it and give you a chance to get some target practice. Before we level out, there is a lugger in the bay. Let's see if you can get them both."

There had been some small-arms fire as Captain Wallace made the strafing runs, and several rounds were heard to strike the aircraft. From 100 feet altitude, the B-24 must have made an enormous target for anyone on the ground with a rifle or sidearm. As Captain Wallace was making the turn around the

Betty, some heavier antiaircraft fire began coming up from the emplacements around the runway at Miri. One twenty-mm cannon shell entered the rear of the bomb bay and fragments slightly wounded the waist gunner and the radar operator. Captain Wallace turned to a heading of ninety degrees and when the aircraft crossed the beach and moved out over open ocean, he spoke into the intercom:

"Pilot to copilot: Come back to cruise power."

"Copilot. Roger. Reducing power to thirty twenty."

"Pilot to crew: Report."

"Bombardier. All bombs on target, Bob. Look at that smoke!"

"Nose Turret. I expended 400 rounds of fifty caliber. I think I got four of those big oil storage tanks."

"Top turret. I put tracers into that Betty and also into the lugger."

"Waist Gunner. I put a lot of rounds into the tanks on the right side of the flight path. We took a shell hit back here. Radar and I have some scratches to show for it."

"Are you okay Waist?"

"Oh, yeah, it's just Band-Aid stuff."

"Radar, are you okay?"

"Roger, sir. Do you want the radar back on?"

"Don't hurry, Radar. Take care of your wounds first."

"Radar. Roger."

"Tail Gunner. I expended all of my ammo. I think I fired three oil tanks."

"Photographer, this is the pilot. Did you get any pictures?"

"Did I ever! I've got pictures that will be in every theater in America!"

Needless to say, Captain Wallace was not censured for his unauthorized deviation from his mission. His success resulted in three more similar mission, a high-altitude photo mission was flown to Lutong to assess the damage. The Thirteenth Air Force Intelligence assessment was that those four airplanes did more damage than four high-altitude missions of four heavy bombardment groups could have done.

The newsreel cameraman was right. His pictures were shown in every theater in the U.S.

Appendix

Late in December 1944, the following report was released by Headquarters Thirteenth Bomber Command:

HEADQUARTERS
XIII BOMBER COMMAND
Intelligence Section
APO 719-2

23 December, 1944

WHAT FOUR SNOOPERS DID TO LUTONG

The Lutong Oil Installation, located in Sarawak Province, Northwest Borneo, is the second most important in Borneo, ranking next to Balikpapan. The area includes a refinery and tank farm at Lutong; the oil fields at Miri, and Seria. The refinery produced nearly 7,000,000 barrels of petroleum products per year in peacetime. Despite fairly complete destruction by evacuating Dutch, the Japanese have repaired the refinery completely and have put the Seria and Miri fields back into production. The importance of the oils which they produce can be used as bunker oil without complicated refining, and the Japs are notoriously low on black oils.

The priority target in this area is the refinery and tank farm at Lutong, concentrated in a compact area about 5/6 of a mile long and 1/6 of a mile wide. The refinery area is 1600' × 840', consisting of two Trumble units which contain fractionating columns, shell stills, condensers and batteries of small receiving tanks. A boiler house, two pump houses and agitators are located within the refinery area. Welding and repair shops adjoin the area. A rundown tank farm located east of and adjacent to the refinery consists of one 15', twenty-six 30', five 35', three 45' cylindrical tanks so at the time of the attack there remained three 140', five 110' and three 70' tanks.

Although not as large as any of the Balikpapan refineries, the Lutong installation has taken on added importance as the production at Balikpapan and the shipping in the Makassar Straits has decreased. The Japanese were shoved further to the west and Lutong is on their new shipping route. Although Lutong is within range of B-24 formations, other requirements prevented a large strike. However our mission included shipping searches along the northwestern and western coasts of Borneo. With the decrease in shipping, secondary land targets were often hit as unloading grounds. Lutong refinery area was one of the best of these targets. Up to 8 December, however, it had not been touched.

At 0750 hours on 8 December, as the sun was just coming up, a lone Liberator of the 868th bombardment Squadron (H), dropped down to 100 feet, made a bombing run across the refinery, dropped his 15 × 250 pound bombs on the cracking plant, then proceeded to make six strafing runs on the oil storage north of the refinery. A Betty on Miri Airdrome to the south and a lugger in the bay were also strafed. 1600 rounds of .50 caliber machine gun ammunition were also expended. The cracking plant was left in flames with smoke rising to 15,000 feet and the fire could be seen for 75 miles. Oblique photos showed six oil storage tanks on fire. At 1353 hours, another Liberator passed the refinery and took photos which showed one 125', five 110' and two 70' oil tanks to be on fire. The Japs didn't take this damage quietly. The anti-aircraft was medium and light, intense and accurate, putting twenty 7.7 mm and 13.2 mm machine gun holes in the aircraft. A 20 mm shell entered the plane through the bulkhead at the back of the bomb bay and exploded, slightly injuring two of the crew.

Those fires were still burning when another blow was struck on 10 December. At 0730 hours, another lone Snooper came in over the refinery at 80 feet, dropped his bombs through the cracking plant, scoring hits on one of the Trumble units and the boiler house. Large fires were started which added to the smoke already coming from the previously set fires. Expending approximately 1500 rounds of .50 calibre ammunition, four strafing runs were made against the storage tanks. It was reported that one large oil tank exploded, one small oil tank exploded, and two large oil tanks were set afire. Although other tanks were hit, they did not burn. Antiaircraft was again medium and light, intense and accurate, resulting in 30 machine gun holes in the aircraft together with two 20 mm hits in the wing and under the waist window. One 20 mm shell entered the ship through the bomb bay, ricocheted off the mount of the hand fuel pump, entered the waist and burst when it struck the Radar Operator's flak helmet injuring him in the arm and face. Every window in the barracks was emitting small arms fire. Hazy photographs showed two large fires, but no accurate interpretation could be made.

Two days later, 12 December, another lone Snooper attacked at 0717 hours. He came in on the deck at 100 ft., dropped 9 × 500 pound incendiary bombs and strafed on the run. The bombs fell in the rundown tanks and refinery area starting two fires, a large one in the refinery and a small one in the tank area. One tank was fired by strafing, two were hit but did not burn. Again, the anti-aircraft fire was accurate and left the aircraft with 6 holes and a 3 supercharger shot out.

On the same day, a special mission was flown by the 868th Squadron to photograph the Lutong area. At 1115 hours, photos were taken and 30 × 100 pound bombs dropped from 4000 feet through the rundown tanks east of the refinery. 3 small tanks were hit but no fires were visible.

The cumulative damage interpretation from the photos shows that in Trumble Unit 2, a 50' × 45' section of the 115 × 45' building containing the furnace was destroyed. One 30' × 45', one 20' × 15' and one 10' × 10' building were destroyed, and one 25' × 25' ground reservoir damaged. Although there were visible craters in the area occupied by the unit, there is no visible damage to the fractionating column, rundown tanks and coolers. In Trumble Unit 3, the 90' × 45' building housing the furnaces was damaged and 2 of the 3 smoke stacks were destroyed. The adjacent fractionating column appears to have been badly damaged. One 25' × 20' pump house was damaged. The main boiler house and an adjacent 70' × 20' house were damaged. One 15' × 10' building adjacent to the rundown tank farm pumphouse was destroyed and one 60' × 60' shop building was damaged. The fire pumphouse was damaged and one of the four adjacent 20' water tanks was badly damaged. The steam and oil lines within the refinery area have been badly damaged, and in some places destroyed. Besides the ten 110' and three 70' cylindrical storage tanks that were destroyed by evacuating forces, three 110' and one 70' tanks were damaged. One 40' storage tank in the rundown tank farm was damaged.

Not all of the damage can be picked up by photo interpretation, especially in the refinery area, and although oblique photos showed fires in storage tanks, damage was not apparent from later coverage. This damage is not included in the above.

It is not possible to compare the results of the bombing and strafing of these four B-24's with any other mission, a recapitulation of the Balikpapan damage may be interesting. A total of 280 B-24's hit Balikpapan, concentrating on the three refineries of Pandansari, paraffin and lube oil and Edeleanu. The Edeleanu plant was destroyed by demolishing Unit 1 and adjacent boiler house, and damaging Unit 2 and the Sulpher Dioxide plant. This effectively put the plant out of action until it can be rebuilt. The Pandansari refinery was put out of action, but is capable of repair. Although most of the installations were destroyed the two vital installations, the boiler and fractionating towers were not destroyed the boiler is possibly damaged and one tower may have been slightly damaged). Three of the four storage tanks were destroyed. The paraffin and Lube Oil Refinery was damaged, not seriously, and is capable of fairly quick repair. The ends of the cooling installation were destroyed and the central portion damaged along with the boilerhouse, powerhouse, pumphouse and grease plant. The bulk of the refinery, including the tanks, agitators, wax presses, high vacuum units, and distilling units, is damaged. Temporary stoppage may have been caused by broken lines and fires, but this refinery must be regarded as still capable of operation after minor repairs. The oil storage facilities have not been lessened by destruction of 3 storage tanks and damage to 3 others in the Pantjoer tank farm.

It is also interesting to note that, based upon the results obtained at Balikpapan, the Lutong refinery and tank farm was analysed by Operational Analysts who stated, "A strike made up of 48 aircraft, each with 9×500 pound general purpose bombs with .025 second tail fuzing has an even chance of causing at least the following damage: A. hitting 5-6 tanks in the storage area. B. Destroying some 90% of the installations in the refinery area, including 2-3 rundown tanks. C. Doing an undetermined amount of damage to installations not visible in vertical photos (such as pipe lines and valve junctions) and to areas surrounding the target area.

IT WAS ALL DONE BY 4 SNOOPERS!

s-Robert Totten
t-ROBERT TOTTEN
Colonel, Air Corps
AC of S, A-2

A TRUE COPY

STUART BALDWIN
1st Lt., Air Corps.
Intelligence Officer

Epilogue

September 1988

This account has been written forty-four years after the facts. It was only possible to reconstruct many of the details of the Snooper operations by referring to the actual mission reports and the *Snooper News* published by Dr. Vince Splane, twice a year from November 1972 until 1988. Some descriptive material was extracted from *From Fiji through the Philippines with the Thirteenth Air Force,* Published by Newsfoto Publishing Company, Angelo, Texas, in 1948.

The Japanese operations and equipment were described in *The Divine Wind,* a Bantam war book, and *Samurai Pilot.*

The mission reports that were used as the factual background for the missions that have been described generally carried the names of first pilots only. The other crew members were not generally named unless one was wounded or killed in the mission. The names of many but not all of the crew members were located by sorting through the photographs that were taken of the crews beside their airplanes for inclusion in the squadron historical files, but there were crews who, for some unknown reason, did not identify all of the members on the photographs. When an unidentified crew member was involved in one of the operations chosen for inclusion in this story, an attempt was made to find the name by corresponding with other members of the squadron who might have remembered. This was not always successful, so there are some crew members who are misnamed in the narratives.

To try to include operations covered by the more than 300 mission reports that have been located in air force files would have made a document that was completely unmanageable, but there was a list in the *Snooper News* of all the first pilots who were found on mission reports. I will include the list here to be complete in giving credit to a highly motivated group.

868th Commanding Officers:

Leo J. Foster	August 1943–August 19, 1944
James D. Barlow	August 20, 1944–December 29, 1944
John R. Knight	December 29, 1944–January 6, 1945
James D. Barlow	January 7, 1945–March 10, 1945
Bayliss E. Harriss	March 10, 1945–End of War

Pilots listed on Mission Reports:

Original Pilots of the Wright Project:

Major Leo J. Foster, Commanding Officer

Major Fran B. Carlson

Captain Robert W. Lehti: Stopped flying after about six weeks. Crew taken over by Major Foster. Major Foster's crew taken over by Lt. Vince Splane.

Captain John F. Zinn, Jr.: Promoted to major and transferred to the 307th Group. Before leaving, he checked out his copilot, Lt. Charles V. Conrad, and Lieutenant Splane as first pilots.

Capt. Franklin T. E. Reynolds

1st Lt. Robert F. Easterling: This crew was lost after making contact with a convoy. The last word heard from them was that they were attacking the convoy.

1st Lt. Charles L. Rockwood

1st Lt. Kenneth E. Brown

1st Lt. Frederick A Martus: This crew was lost in a crash at Guadalcanal while returning from attacking convoy. It was believed that the pilot was dead as a result of enemy anti-aircraft fire.

1st Lt. George A. Tillinghast: Stopped flying after approximately six weeks. Crew taken over by Lt. Durward F. Sumner, who was brought in from the 307th Bomb Group.

1st Pilots in October 1943:

Lt. V. D. Splane
Lt. C. V. Conrad
Lt. D. F. Sumner

1st Replacement Crews on Guadalcanal, November 1943:

Lt. Arthur Deland

Lt. Donald E. Thompson: Crashed after takeoff from Noemfoor, September 19, 1944. Five crew members killed, seven survived including Thompson and D. W. Barry.

Lt. Federick C. Bryan

Next replacement crews:

Lt. Richard A. Gay: Crashed after takeoff from Munda, March 20, 1944. Three survivors: Toole, copilot; Lamica, engineer; and Dyer, radar operator.

Lt. Thomas B. Arthur: Lost over Truk, April 1944.

Lt. Robert A. Robbins: Crew lost when plane crashed into Rendova, March 1944.

Lt. Kenneth R. King: Failed to return from Rabaul, March 11, 1944.

Lt. Peter S. Colt: Crashed on takeoff from Noemfoor, September 22, 1944. One survivor.

Lt. Charles Binford

Lt. Phillip A. Hoffman

Lt Robert J. Alsop

Lt. Robert E. Rauch: Made water landing while returning from attack on Palau, May 5, 1944. Three killed. Crashed on takeoff from Los Negros, July 16, 1944, two killed.

Lt. Irving G. Booth: After attacking Truk, ran out of gas and made night water landing. Three survived. June 1944.

Lt. Wilson Nicholas

Lt. Don W. Dyer: Shot down in flames over Truk, June 11, 1944.

Lt. Jack L. Wagner: Shot down over Truk, June 12, 1944.

Lt. Louis Beck

Lt. Wilmer B. Haynes: Lost over Truk, June 25, 1944.

Lt. Dwight D. Barry: Crashed on takeoff from Morotai, March 10, 1945. Twelve killed, one survivor: Carl Daye.

Lt. Eric E. Muller: Crashed September 24, 1944, during landing attempt at Morotai. Three killed.

Capt. Robert D. Wallace: Nose gunner killed while strafing Puerto Pricessa harbor October, 1944. Gunner killed, copilot and navigator wounded while preparing for takeoff from Morotai on November 23, 1944. Brought home two wounded on December 8, 1944, after attacking Lutong refinery. Aircraft hole in thirty-three places.

Capt. Earle M. Smith: Brought home radar operator wounded after eighty-ft altitude strafing run on Lutong oil refinery December 10, 1944; aircraft holed in thirty places. December 13, 1944, brought home copilot mortally wounded, navigator wounded, after strafing and bombing Lutong refinery from 100 feet. January 10, 1945, brought home four wounded crew members after an attack on Labuan. Although wounded himself, made a crash landing on Morotai with one main gear collapsed.

Lt. George E. Thompson: All members of the crews lost December 14, 1944.

Lt. Nichol

Lt. Green Wadsworth: Brought home Lt. Matt Ernser with most of his left foot shot away.

Lt. George L. Cooke: January 26, 1945, brought home his airplane with two engines out and no nose wheel, no injuries.

Lt. Courtney L. Richardson

Lt. Morgan

Maj. James Kendrick

Lt. Robert P. Thompson

Lt. John W. Greene: Crashed December 14, 1944; ten killed, two survivors.

Lt. John W. Workman

Captain Townsend Rogers

Lt. William H. Beaver: April 21, 1945, rammed by a Japanese fighter, no survivors.

Lt. Robert C. Upfield

Lt. William F. Plunkett: Failed to return January 14, 1945, from attack on Sanga oil fields.

Lt. Robert J. Albert

Lt. Herman R. Bartlemes

Lt. Phillip M. Whitehead

Lt. Harry Lee: Killed with three others in an operational accident February 7, 1945.

Lt. Fred M. Olsen

Lt. Maurice R. McDaniel: Killed September in crash of a C-47.

Lt. Royal A. Putnam

Lt. Richard S. Cole

Lt. John C. Priest

Lt. Frank M. Reidy

Lt. Gus Smitherman

Lt. Edward B. Mills, Jr.: Last crew to be lost during WWII: August 7, 1945.

Lt. Henson G. Sprawls: Flew last attack mission of WWII August 7, 1945.

Lt. Robert N. Ellingson

Lt. Eugene Maggioncalda

Lt. Walter N. Low: July 23, 1945, due to battle damage, crew bailed out. Pilot, navigator, and bombardier were the only survivors.

Lieutenant Probets

Lt. Don Gilman

Lt. L. Lewellen

Lieutenant Mingo

Lieutenant Whitesell

Lieutenant Hendricks

Lieutenant Graitzer

Lt. Glenn Cooper

Lt. Marlin Arford

Lieutenant Harter: All members of the crew lost over Mandei, June 20, 1945.

Lt. Stephen Ober: June 19, 1945, attacked by Japanese fighters. Lt. Russell killed and Gifford Hampshire wounded.

Lt. Milford Jensen

Lt. George Koonsman

Lt. Donald R. Callison: July 25, 1945, fuel shortage caused the crew to bail out one hour from base. Pilot, copilot, radar operator and two gunners survived. Five crew members lost.

Lt. Daniel B. Vermilya

Lt. Bernard E. Toole

Lt. Robert H. Nagel

Lt. Fred J. Ryan

Lt. Wayne E. Putnam

Capt. Robert M. Chalmers

Lt. Robert F. Marcotte: Crashed into a mountain July 17, 1945. One survivor.

Lt. Arthur J. Frahm

Lt. Alexander R. Mackenzie

Lt. Donald L. McClintock

Major Garvin

Crews listed on the roster at the end of the war:

Lt. George G. Grupe III
Lt. Jack B. Shattuck
Lt. Wallace J. Palmer
Lt. Warren R. Hoover
Lt. Richard D. Elston
Lt. Donald E. Sark